Elinor M. Brent-Dyer's

Chalet School

Additional material by Helen McClelland

An Armada Original

First published in Great Britain in Armada in 1989

Armada is an imprint of the Children's Division,
part of the Collins Publishing Group,
8 Grafton Street, London W1X 3LA

The publishers are grateful to W. & R. Chambers Ltd
and Mrs Chloë Rutherford for their permission to
reproduce extracts and illustrations from many of the
Chalet School books by Elinor M. Brent-Dyer.
Without their co-operation this book
would have been impossible.

Printed and bound in Great Britain
by The Eagle Press Plc, Glasgow

CONTENTS

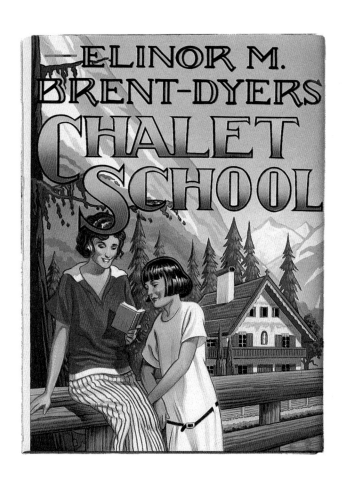

INTRODUCTION

Elinor Brent-Dyer's Chalet School is nearly sixty-five years old. Today's enthusiastic readers could be, and sometimes are, the grandchildren of those who enjoyed the books when they first appeared, and the Chalet School paperbacks published by Armada continue to sell at the astonishing rate of between 150,000 and 200,000 copies each year.

Why should these particular books have retained their popularity in such a remarkable way? In the past there were other popular series of children's books, both comparable and contemporary with the Chalet School stories, and most of these have now disappeared. So why were the Chalet School books among the few that resisted the downward trend? Why are they now virtually the only survivors from the pre-war golden age of the school-story that are still regularly bought and widely read today, and by both children and adults? The most devoted Chalet School fan might be hard put to find a quick answer. And anyway, what kind of people are they who become Chalet School fans today, at the threshold of the 1990s? Their number and enthusiasm are beyond question: not only do they buy up those thousands of paperbacks and scour the secondhand market for out-of-print hardbacks, they even devote time to writing the fan letters which continue to this day to flow in a steady stream from around the world.

Says one fan, Rosie Veitch: "I can remember my first encounter with a Brent-Dyer story – it was in the 1970s, and the title was *The Chalet School Triplets*. Shortly after I

One of the hundreds of fan letters Elinor received

Chalet at Pertisau, in the Austrian Tirol

Pertisau (Briesau)

found it in a small branch library in the north east of England, Chalet School stories became incredibly difficult to find – they even began to disappear from the libraries. Suddenly, tragedy struck: a fire in our school library destroyed *The Highland Twins at the Chalet School* and *The Chalet School and the Island – before I'd read them.* Now, after fifteen years, I am the proud owner of 35 hardback Brent-Dyers – but it wasn't until I'd reached university that I was able to come out of the closet about my obsession. There's something terribly embarrassing about being seen in the children's department of a bookshop while in your teens! I was surprised to find that I got a lot of sympathy from many of my fellows at university, though I'm sure others thought I was slightly strange – and probably still do!"

What kind of person was Elinor Brent-Dyer, that she was able to produce books to which so many people were and still are drawn? And where did she get the idea for her amazingly successful series? The last question is easier to answer than some of the others. It all began in the summer of 1924 when Elinor Brent-Dyer had spent a long and immensely enjoyable holiday in the Austrian Tirol. On her return – or perhaps even while she was there – she decided to use Austria as the setting for a school-story "with a difference"; and this book, *The School at the Chalet*, was published the following year by W. & R. Chambers who were among the leading publishers of school-stories at this time. Many of the places Elinor had visited during her holiday are described in the early Chalet School books, and can be identified without much difficulty. For the Chalet School's original Tirolean location at "Briesau" on the shores of the "Tiernsee" really does exist, complete with the little mountain railway, the lake steamers,

The village of Pertisau, which in the Chalet School books became Briesau

The dust jacket of Elinor's first Chalet School book, illustrated by Nina K. Brisley

and other features of the district made familiar by the stories. But in real life the village of "Briesau" has another name, as do both the lake itself, and the town at the foot of the mountains which is the starting point for the little cog-wheel train (see *Locations*, page 24).

The School at the Chalet was not Elinor Brent-Dyer's first book. Some years before her visit to Austria she had become friendly with a theatrical husband-and-wife team, Edith and Julian Bainbridge. Hazel, the Bainbridge's ten-year-old daughter, was a talented child actress, and she and Elinor were to become great friends despite the wide difference in their ages. One of the things Hazel most enjoyed was listening to the wonderful stories that Elinor could tell. And it was specially for Hazel that Elinor wrote *Gerry Goes to School*, her first published book. She was devoted to Hazel, whom she often called her little "adopted sister" – the same phrase Joey uses in the books about Robin Humphries. So possibly the character of "the Robin", though not directly a portrait, may owe something to Hazel.

Present-day readers are unlikely to come across *Gerry Goes to School*, because it and the six other books belonging to a set known as the "La Rochelle" series have been out of print for many years. However, these books do survive in a link with the Chalet School, because many of the characters from "La Rochelle" appear later in the Chalet series.

Elinor followed *Gerry* with two other books, one being *The Maids of La Rochelle*, the first of her Channel Islands stories. All three enjoyed a moderate success. But no one could possibly have foreseen in October 1925, when *The School at the Chalet* first appeared, just how widely and enduringly popular this book (with, later, its multitude of successors) was going to prove.

The first in Elinor's *La Rochelle* series

Nor could the author have had the remotest inkling that she had set off, that October of 1925, along a road that would continue for the next forty-four years, ending only with her death in September 1969. During that time the Chalet School series was to reach the staggering total of fifty-eight full length hardback books and one shorter paperback (see *Questions* page 95), and the stories were to gain a wide and faithful following. Quantities of fan mail would arrive from many distant parts of the English-speaking world as well as from Chalet School enthusiasts all over Britain. Elinor would make frequent appearances at Book Exhibitions up and down

By its final year, the Chalet Club had over 4000 members. It was disbanded after Elinor's death in 1969

Chalet Club
News Letter

Issue N

December 1961

11 THISTLE

Dear Club Members,

I expect you have been wondering when you are going to get this letter. I thought it would you have it just before the Christmas holidays, as I know you are all very busy during term find some good ideas here for Christmas shopping. I am going to ask my Publishers to let y list of the available Chalet School books and in the same printed catalogue you will find som ion about books for Christmas.

In this News Letter you will see the latest news of our competitions, another 'Chalet Scho you will try for your Christmas Party), and, of course, my answers to correspondents. I hav ing letters from you and I only wish we could include answers to everyone. Unfortunatel that.

By now I expect you will know that the new chronicle of the Chalet School is in all the bookshops and libraries —THE CHALET SCHOOL W hope you all enjoy it. And don jacket? It strikes me as one c have had. In the correspond that one of our Members suggestion for preserving t' that I had intended maki this treatment for the Ch all the other good books

Talking of dust-jacket have written to me abc As we seem to have qu among our members, I a to help in this line.

First of all, rememb illustrate the story, so fu the characters you cho has straight hair, for in waves. Don't, if you a make her look as if she quite a difference betwee girls that you know au heroine is described as s on a wall. It is details to look out to make you

Now I have said enough hope it will help all you peo

The Chalet Club *invites you...*

Chalet Club News letter

May 1959

Issue No. 1

TO THE MEMBERS OF THE CHALET SCHOOL CLUB

Well, here it is at last! Our own Club for those who enjoy the Chalet School Series!

I have had so many, many letters during the years the Series has been running. Letters from England, Scotland, Ireland and Wales. Letters from Canada, Australia, New Zealand, The Barbadoes, India, France, Belgium, Switzerland, South Africa, Kenya, and other places I have answered all

the country, and was to be interviewed in the *Tonight* programme on television. There was even to be a Chalet School Club – something unique in the history of the girls' school-story: this ran successfully from May 1959 until Elinor Brent-Dyer's death some ten years later, its membership then numbering nearly 4,000 fans. (And today, a further twenty years on, the club has a successor in the recently founded Chalet School Club of Victoria, Australia.) A final accolade: when she died Elinor was considered important enough to be given obituary notices in many of the national papers, among them an appreciative half-column in *The Times*.

How odd to think that at the time of her visit to the Tirol she was just an unknown schoolteacher who had happened to choose Austria for her long summer holiday. But then it was Elinor's reactions to the Tirol that inspired the whole enterprise, while it was her affection for Austria, in particular for "Briesau" and the "Tiernsee" that continued to colour her approach to the series, even after the Chalet School had moved elsewhere. And the Tirolean setting of the early books usually comes high on the list when fans are asked their reasons for enjoying the stories. Elinor's "Briesau-am-Tiernsee" had caught her readers' imaginations not only because of its beauty but because it was fun. Who would not prefer to forsake the ordinary bus or train and travel to school by that "quaint little mountain railway", and then in the "little white steamer" across the lake, with breathtaking views on every side?

In this delightful setting the most routine school activities – walks, for instance – can seem glamorous; while the extraordinary adventures – two girls getting lost in the mist on a mountain precipice, or the Chalet being engulfed by floods during the spring thaw – appear credible, given the school's alpine situation.

Besides, right from the beginning, the Chalet School had the advantage of being "different", with its mixture of nationalities and religious denominations, its near-family atmosphere (at least in the early books) and its delicious-sounding meals.

Another facet of the books that appealed to many was mentioned by a schoolgirl, who wrote to Elinor that: "In reading the French conversation of the Chalet girls, unknowingly I learnt quite a few words, phrases and idioms. . ."; and although Elinor's own knowledge of French and German was apparently limited (she sometimes makes glaring errors in both languages!), there is no doubt that her stories really have encouraged many schoolgirls to try and emulate the prowess of trilingual Joey Bettany and her friends.

Nevertheless, in spite of all this, it is plain that had there been no more to the books than a glamorous background – not only in Austria, but in the Channel Islands, Herefordshire, Wales, and Switzerland – the Chalet School series would long ago have been forgotten. That the Chalet School continues to survive after more than sixty years is mainly a tribute to the entertaining stories, the sense of comedy and fun, and above all to the characterisation shown in the early books. Here, the pupils are neither the paragons of virtue nor the monsters of depravity that are found in some school-stories, but credible schoolgirls, who may have a rather unusual number of adventures but still manage

Joyce Linton

to behave and talk like human beings.

In fact, Elinor's principal achievement would seem to lie in having created at the beginning of her series, where it mattered most, a set of characters who gradually assumed an almost independent existence in her eyes and those of her readers. Then, by employing various devices, she was able to keep at least the most important of these characters on stage throughout the series. Later their multitudinous children were to follow in their footsteps at the school, often learning from the same teachers as had their parents. And what amounts to a personal relationship between readers and characters was slowly to be established.

Plenty of reasons then to show why readers once hooked will often begin to feel, as Joey did, that "the Chalet School must go on". It would be harder to explain precisely what qualities in the books have turned so many first-time readers into addicts. But it happens every day.

THE TIROLEAN YEARS

A typical Tirolean chalet

"Ringed round by mountains, with a long narrow valley stretching away to the west, and water meadows at its southern extremity, the Tiern See in the North Tirol is surely one of the loveliest places in the world, and an ideal spot for such a school as the Chalet School." Here, Miss Madge Bettany had established her school, "beginning with nine pupils . . . ."

In fact there had originally been only three: Joey Bettany, Madge's much younger sister; 14-year-old Grizel Cochrane, who was two years older than Jo but had previously been attending the same school in England; and Simone Lecoutier, cousin of Mademoiselle Lepâttre, the Frenchwoman who was Madge Bettany's partner in her brave enterprise. But the Chalet School was destined to be lucky and, by the time the first day arrived, these three had been joined by six Tirolean girls: Gisela Marani and her little sister Maria; Bernhilda and Frieda Mensch; Bette Rincini and Gertrud Steinbrücke. Gisela, at sixteen the oldest and most responsible of the group, was soon to be chosen by Miss Bettany as the Chalet School's first head girl; and all nine girls, Joey Bettany in particular, were in due course to become pillars of the school and to play roles of some importance throughout the series.

This pattern of steadily growing numbers was always to be a feature of the school's history (with the exception of one short period during the war years). At the end of the first term there were eighteen girls, and the staff had been increased by the arrival of Miss Maynard to teach mathematics; while Herr Anserl, the gruff but golden-hearted Austrian piano professor, had become a regular weekly visitor – two more names that would recur until the end of the series.

By the second term, the total had risen to more than thirty pupils, representing many different nationalities; and new staff included Miss Durrant, who introduces the school to folk dancing, and the eccentric Mr Tristan Denny; the latter would still be taking his inspirational if sometimes hair-raising singing classes more than fifty books later, for he was to follow the school through all its travels.

And so it continued. Despite alarms and excursions – for adventures of many kinds were never lacking at the Chalet School – the numbers went on and on growing. During Joey Bettany's last school year there were upwards of a hundred girls. And the year after that a spectacular increase took place, when the Chalet School joined forces with St Scholastika's – a school situated then on the other side of the Tiernsee, which at one time had been a deadly rival.

Present-day views of Achensee, the original Tiernsee, and map of the surrounding area

After this amalgamation, the "new" Chalet School found itself with nearly 250 pupils and a combined teaching staff so large that another chalet had to be found to house them.

By this time the number of buildings occupied by the school had also increased considerably. The original chalet – "a very large wooden building which had been designed for a hotel" – with its wonderful views of the lake and mountains, was always to be the school's main premises; but, before the second term began, a smaller house was purchased for use by the Juniors. This lay at a short distance from the main school and was known for some years as Le Petit Chalet. A school hall was built during the summer holidays in the third year; laboratories and a domestic economy room were added at various times. Then, just before Joey's last term at school, a new chalet was custom-built in the school grounds: this was designed for the Middle School (those notorious Middles!) and was dedicated to St Clare; the Petit Chalet being now renamed St Agnes's and the original house Ste Thérèse's.

Yet another house was required when the Chalet School absorbed its former rival, and for this new building the name St Scholastika's was retained. The recently acquired staff house, mentioned above, was given the name St Hild's – Madge Russell (the former Miss Bettany) having decreed that an English saint should be honoured this time; presumably she had in mind St Hild of Whitby, whose shrine is situated not far from Elinor Brent-Dyer's own childhood home in the north-east of England.

In addition to all these houses on the original site, there was also the Chalet School Annexe. This – a special unit that had been established on the Sonnalpe during the school's fifth year – catered for particularly delicate children as well

Bedroom in a Tirolean inn, with one of Elinor's famous "plumeaus" on the bed

as for some whose parents were patients at the nearby sanatorium. Here the headmistress was Juliet Carrick, who had been a pupil at the Chalet School during its first two years and was the first old girl to join the staff.

Naturally the school's complement of teachers (always referred to as mistresses – or masters – at the Chalet School) had also grown steadily as the terms went by. Among important figures who appear early and remain to the end are Miss Wilson, Miss Annersley – she of the beautiful speaking voice and renowned eyesight – and Matron Lloyd who becomes the school's favourite domestic tyrant; also Miss Stewart, although she disappears a few years later to be married.

Inevitably there were changes. In the school's third year Mademoiselle Lepâttre takes over as headmistress, following Madge Bettany's marriage to Doctor James Russell. (It was Doctor Russell who established the sanatorium on the Sonnalpe.) But Mademoiselle's reign, successful though it is, does not last long: three years later she is stricken with a serious illness (which eventually proves fatal); and at the beginning of the 13th book, *The New Chalet School*, the school learns that Miss Annersley has now been appointed headmistress in her place.

The Chalet School, then, by its final year in the Tirol, had grown in size from just three to about 250 pupils, had a large teaching staff, and was currently occupying six different houses. It had also become a truly international school, with at least ten European nations being represented in addition to the British, and several pupils from the United States.

Traditions were always to be considered important. They, too, were of rapid growth; and by the end of the years in the Tirol the Chalet School way of life was firmly on the lines that have become so familiar to readers.

The prefect system, to which Miss Bettany (and plainly Elinor, too) attached great importance, was inaugurated within a few weeks of the school's opening. And from the very beginning, cold baths – from which the girls somehow contrive to emerge "glowing from the icy sting of the mountain water" – were the order of the day; beds had to be meticulously stripped, plumeaus to be aired; and woe betide any girl who had so much as a button missing if Matron's eye should fall on her – as it always did!

No girls should ever have complained of boredom. Before the end of the first year, folk dancing, the Hobbies Club, the school magazine (the *Chaletian*), and much musical activity in addition to choral singing – these were all in full swing. *The Youngest Shepherd*, first of the annual Christmas plays, had marked 13-year-old Joey Bettany's singing debut. Guides and Brownies were started early in the second year, which also saw the founding of the sanatorium on the Sonnalpe, and the beginning of the hospital's long association with the school. Very soon a Sale of Work in aid of the san becomes an annual event.

Another custom that gets off to an early start is the tireless crusade against the use of slang expressions, a war that would be carried on throughout Chalet School history. And during the Christmas term following *The Princess of the Chalet School* (or so it can be deduced – see note on missing Chalet School books, page 94), those dreaded days are introduced when speaking in French or German is compulsory for all, staff and pupils, lessons and play-times alike. Presumably the days in between, when only English was allowed, were pretty tough for the other nationalities, although they always seemed to cope rather better.

All these traditions and customs, plus others

too numerous to mention, were to endure not only through this early part of Chalet School history but right to the end of the series. They were moreover to survive the many upheavals and migrations that characterise the next phase of the story, which begins with the fourteenth book, *The Chalet School in Exile*.

THE CHALET SCHOOL ON THE MOVE

The opening of *The Chalet School in Exile* sees the first of many changes when the school, after being happily settled at the Tiernsee for between seven and eight years, has to move hurriedly up to the Sonnalpe, following the Nazi annexation of Austria. But this temporary home, in the former hotel Der Edel Ritter, lasts only a few months as the political situation soon makes things impossible. And now for a time the Chalet School ceases to exist. Joey and a handful of the others, who have fallen foul of the Gestapo, make a perilous escape through the mountains to Switzerland, and later to the island of Guernsey.

Here, against all odds, a house is eventually found near Jerbourg (see *Locations* p.43); and although numbers at first are reduced to 52 the school gradually struggles back to life. Many old friends from the Tirolean days, both girls and staff, are reunited, including Miss Wilson, Miss Annersley and "Matey"; and Simone Lecoutier and Grizel Cochrane are among old girls who join the teaching staff.

Joey, in the intervening year, has married Jack Maynard, one of the doctors at the sanatorium (it, too, has removed to Guernsey). And during the first term in Guernsey a major stir is caused by the arrival of Joey's triplet daughters.

Unfortunately the time in Guernsey is short. Once the war starts, the Channel Islands can no longer be considered a safe refuge, especially when the Germans look set to occupy the French coast. So yet again the school must be uprooted. But at least this time the new premises they find

Jerbourg Pine Forest, Guernsey

Petit Port, St Martin, Guernsey

at Plas Howell in Armishire (see *Locations* p.44) are to remain their home through the next seven books, and about eight school years. It is here that the custom of having compulsory French and German days is re-introduced – amid a fair amount of groans and grumbles!

School life continues to be filled with activities old and new. Maybe the local hills can hardly compare with the Alps, but there are still energetic walks to be taken, not to mention hop-picking in the fields round about. And one winter some girls manage to commemorate the old Tirolean days by getting lost in the snow. The new interest in gardening, dating from the time in Guernsey, is steadily maintained all through and endures also after the war, when the Chalet girls were all encouraged to "Dig for Victory".

All round a happy time; but defective drains are found to be causing illness in the school, and yet another move is required.

As always, the school is lucky, and in the nick of time a suitably large house is offered, situated on the island of St Briavel (see *Locations* p.45). Here, seven of the eight books from No. 21 to No. 28 inclusive, are to be set. The exception is No. 26, *The Chalet School in the Oberland*; this describes the school's first venture into Switzerland, when a small group goes to set up a finishing branch; and the events take place during the same term as those at St Briavel which were recounted in No. 25, *Shocks for the Chalet School*.

No. 28, *Changes For The Chalet School*, paves the way for a last removal – it really is to prove the final one. This time the school's destination is the Görnetz Platz in the Bernese Oberland (see *Locations* p.62). A number of the girls, including all the Juniors, are to remain in Britain, where they will be housed at Carnbach on the Welsh coast; but the end of

this book sees about a hundred of the Seniors and Middles all set for travel to Switzerland, and preparing to don a new school uniform in gentian blue.

Throughout the long period of migration the Chalet School has faithfully maintained the traditions and customs that were established during the early years. One new one had been added, one that came about before the escape from Austria: this was the Chalet School Peace League, with its high ideals of international fellowship and understanding. This, like the ecumenical attitude of the school, was something considerably in advance of its time.

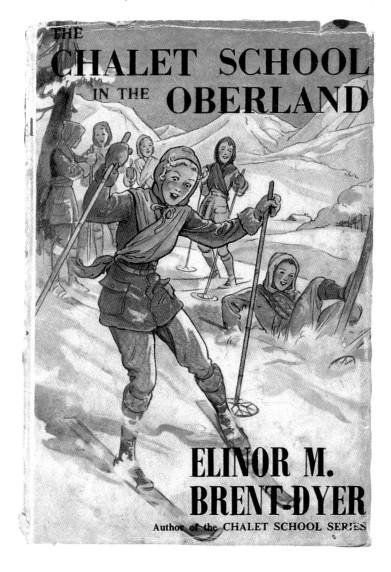

THE SWISS YEARS

The third part of the series, comprising books Nos. 29 to 58, contains a larger number of books than either of the other two, but covers only about eight school years, with four titles quite often relating to a single year.

The first of the batch, No. 29, *Joey Goes to the Oberland*, is not really a school-story but is concerned with the Maynard family's long roundabout journey to Switzerland, where they arrive a short time before the school turns up in force. This book leads straight into No. 30, *The Chalet School and Barbara*, which provides the first act proper for the school's Swiss drama. But then, somewhat misleadingly, the next book, *Tom Tackles The Chalet School*, is what Elinor would have called a "hop-out-of-kin", since it was published out of chronological order and belongs in fact to the Armishire part of the series.

After this the stories, from 32 onwards, follow each other in correct chronological order. But in three other books the action, for the most part, happens outside Switzerland. These are: No. 43, *Joey & Co. in Tirol*; and No. 47, *A Future Chalet School Girl*; both being holiday stories, set mainly in the Tiernsee district, the Chalet School's original home; and No. 39, *The Coming of Age of the Chalet School*, in which the latter part describes a visit to the Tiernsee by members of the school and various old girls.

For the school, the years in Switzerland prove to be as action-packed as any in their history.

The alpine terrain provides the opportunity for the girls once again to enjoy long walks and scrambles in the clear mountain air; and, with the coming of the snow, to take part in winter sports – a new experience for most.

To begin with, they find that the number of girls has dwindled to a mere hundred or so. But in no time the total starts creeping up again. Three years later there are 200 girls; and, by the final year of the chronicle, the all-time record has been reached of more than 300 pupils at the Görnetz Platz, while the branch at Carnbach in Wales has over a hundred.

The staff now includes a greater than ever number of old girls, with Biddy O'Ryan, Peggy Burnett, Rosalie Dean, Hilary Burn and Nancy Wilmot among them at various times. The turnover is fairly rapid, for members of the Chalet School teaching staff often leave to get married – usually to doctors.

Old girls are also represented in a different way among the pupils, of whom a sizable proportion are now the children of former Chaletians. Joey Bettany/Maynard and her close friends Frieda, Marie, and Simone, are only a few of those whose daughters appear at the school.

Miss Annersley and Miss Wilson – for some time now Co-Head – remain to the end. And Joey always manages to find time, despite the demands of her enormous family and busy writing career, to take part enthusiastically in most of the school's activities.

These latter include the traditional half-term excursions, which now range throughout Switzerland; the annual Christmas plays; the staff evenings and form entertainments; and of course the Sales of Work – presented ever more elaborately, and raising ever greater sums of money in aid of the san, which had preceded the school to the Görnetz Platz, and with whom close links were always maintained.

Finally, mention should be made of two important anniversaries that occur during the years in Switzerland. The first is the Chalet School's 21st birthday: this is celebrated in a variety of ways, as described in *The Coming of Age of the Chalet School*. The other is the school's Silver Jubilee. And since this fictional occasion happened to coincide with the appearance of Book Number 50 of the series – *The Chalet School Reunion* – the occasion was also celebrated in real life.

The Chalet School Reunion dust jacket, which was taken from the picture Chambers presented to Elinor on the publication of the book

THE TIROL

LOCATIONS · 1

One of the larger lakeside steamers

When Elinor Brent-Dyer chose to spend her 1924 summer holiday in Austria, she can have had no inkling at the time that her choice would affect quite literally the whole future course of her life. Yet it is no exaggeration to state that it did. For had she decided to go somewhere else that summer it is possible that the Chalet School would never have existed, since it was unquestionably her visit to Austria which started the whole mammoth enterprise on its way; while it was her abiding affection for the Tirol, in particular for the strikingly beautiful district where she had stayed, that continued through the years to colour her approach to the Chalet series, acting as a constant stimulus to her imagination.

Of course most Chalet fans in the early years were unaware that the school's Tirolean location, at "Briesau" on the shores of the "Tiernsee", really does exist. But then Elinor had deliberately set out to disguise the identity of the Tiernsee; and for many years she had succeeded in doing this, by changing certain important place names and topographical details. It was probably not until after the war that some among her fans were lucky enough, as I was, to stumble accidentally on the secret. In my case it happened way back in 1950 when I was visiting Austria with my mother. We were staying in Innsbruck, and I had been struggling through a local guide book — my German not being as expert as Joey Bettany's — when my eye was caught by the name Scholastika, a place often mentioned in the early books. It occurred in the section dealing with a lake called the Achensee, and a hurried look at the map revealed other familiar names: Buchau, Seespitz, Seehof, Gaisalm and Eben were all there. In fact, although this lake was not called Tiernsee the only Chalet School place missing from its shores was that of "Briesau" itself. But what if the village called Pertisau was the original "Briesau"? Its lakeside position on a triangular wedge of land running up into the mountains, and situated roughly halfway between Seespitz and Gaisalm, fitted the stories exactly. And although another familiar name, that of the little town "Spärtz", could not be found on the map either, there *was* a town called Jenbach in the right place at the foot of the mountains. Further confirmation: from Jenbach station a cog-wheel railway climbed the mountainside to connect with the Achensee steamers at Seespitz. It had to be right. Jenbach must be "Spärtz"; the Tiernsee in real life was the Achensee and Briesau was Pertisau. The site of the Chalet School really did exist.

Pertisau (Briesau)

Achensee (the Tiernsee)

The "quaint little mountain railway" and the "little white steamer" so often mentioned in the stories

COMPLETE LIST OF TITLES
IN THE CHALET SCHOOL SERIES

Originally the series consisted of 58 full-length stories in hardback and one shorter paperback, all published by W. & R. Chambers Ltd; but numbers 10, 13 and 35 of the original stories were divided for publication in Armada Paperbacks, and the second part of each was then retitled (see below). The following is a complete list of the series, dated and numbered in order of original publication. The number given to Armada editions is shown in brackets. The correct reading order of the stories, where this differs, is given in brackets. Titles in capitals have already been published by Armada, although all may not be currently available. An up-to-date stocklist will be sent on request.

1. (1) THE SCHOOL AT THE CHALET - 1925
2. (2) JO OF THE CHALET SCHOOL - 1926
3. (3) THE PRINCESS OF THE CHALET SCHOOL - 1927
4. (4) THE HEAD GIRL OF THE CHALET SCHOOL - 1928
5. (5) RIVALS OF THE CHALET SCHOOL - 1929
6. (6) EUSTACIA GOES TO THE CHALET SCHOOL - 1930
7. (7) THE CHALET SCHOOL AND JO - 1931
8. (8) THE CHALET GIRLS IN CAMP - 1932
9. (9) EXPLOITS OF THE CHALET GIRLS - 1933
10. The Chalet School and the Lintons – 1934
   Published in two Armada volumes:
   (10) i) THE CHALET SCHOOL AND THE LINTONS
   (11) ii) A REBEL AT THE CHALET SCHOOL
11. (12) THE NEW HOUSE AT THE CHALET SCHOOL - 1935
12. (13) JO RETURNS TO THE CHALET SCHOOL - 1936
13. The New Chalet School – 1938
   Published in two Armada volumes:
   (14) i) THE NEW CHALET SCHOOL
   (15) ii) A UNITED CHALET SCHOOL
14. (16) THE CHALET SCHOOL IN EXILE - 1940
15. (17) THE CHALET SCHOOL AT WAR - 1941 (Title originally: THE CHALET SCHOOL GOES TO IT)
16. (18) THE HIGHLAND TWINS AT THE CHALET SCHOOL - 1942
17. (19) LAVENDER LEIGH AT THE CHALET SCHOOL – 1943 Title originally: LAVENDER LAUGHS IN THE CHALET SCHOOL)
18. (20) GAY LAMBERT AT THE CHALET SCHOOL - 1944 (Title originally: GAY FROM CHINA AT THE CHALET SCHOOL)
19. (21) Jo to the Rescue – 1945
   (22) (19b. TOM TACKLES THE CHALET SCHOOL - 1955
   (23) 19c. THE CHALET SCHOOL AND ROSALIE - 1951)
20. (24) THREE GO TO THE CHALET SCHOOL - 1949
21. (25) THE CHALET SCHOOL AND THE ISLAND - 1950
22. (26) PEGGY OF THE CHALET SCHOOL - 1950
23. (27) CAROLA STORMS THE CHALET SCHOOL - 1951
   (19c) The Chalet School and Rosalie – 1951 (Published out of order, with no official number, See 19c above.)

24. (28) THE WRONG CHALET
          SCHOOL - 1952
25. (29) SHOCKS FOR THE CHA-
          CHALET SCHOOL - 1952
26. (30) THE CHALET SCHOOL
          IN THE OBERLAND -
          1952
          (Events in stories 25 and
          26 occur during the same
          term, in Wales and
          Switzerland respectively.)
27. (31) BRIDE LEADS THE CHA-
          CHALET SCHOOL - 1953
28. (32) Changes for the Chalet
          School – 1953
29. (33) Joey Goes to the Oberland
          – 1954
30. (34) THE CHALET SCHOOL
          AND BARBARA - 1954
31. (19b) TOM TACKLES THE
          CHALET SCHOOL - 1955
          (Published out of order,
          see 19c above.)
32. (35) The Chalet School Does It
          Again – 1955
33. (36) A Chalet Girl from Kenya
          – 1955
34. (37) MARY-LOU OF THE
          CHALET SCHOOL - 1956
35.   A Genius at the Chalet

School – 1956
Published in two Armada
volumes:
     (38) i) A GENIUS AT THE
               CHALET SCHOOL
     (39) ii) THE CHALET SCHOOL
               FETE
36. (40) A PROBLEM FOR THE
          CHALET SCHOOL - 1956
37. (41) THE NEW MISTRESS AT
          THE CHALET SCHOOL -
          1957
38. (42) EXCITEMENTS FOR THE
          CHALET SCHOOL - 1957
39. (43) THE COMING OF AGE
          OF THE CHALET
          SCHOOL - 1958
40. (44) THE CHALET SCHOOL
          AND RICHENDA - 1958
41. (45) TRIALS FOR THE CHA-
          CHALET SCHOOL - 1959
42. (46) THEODORA AND THE
          CHALET SCHOOL - 1959
43. (47) Joey and Co. in Tirol –
          1960
44. (48) RUEY RICHARDSON AT
          THE CHALET SCHOOL -
          1960
          (Title originally: RUEY
          RICHARDSON
          - CHALETIAN)
45. (49) A LEADER IN THE CHA-
          CHALET SCHOOL - 1961
46. (50) THE CHALET SCHOOL
          WINS THE TRICK - 1961
47. (51) A Future Chalet School
          Girl – 1962
48. (52) THE FEUD IN THE CHA-
          CHALET SCHOOL - 1962
49. (53) THE CHALET SCHOOL
          TRIPLETS - 1963
50. (54) The Chalet School Reunion
          – 1963
51. (55) Jane and the Chalet School
          – 1964

52. (56) Redheads at the Chalet
          School – 1964
53. (57) Adrienne and the Chalet
          School – 1965
54. (58) Summer Term at the Chalet
          School – 1965
55. (59) Challenge for the Chalet
          School – 1966
56. (60) Two Sams at the Chalet
          School – 1967
57. (61) Althea Joins the Chalet
          School – 1969
58. (62) Prefects of the Chalet
          School – 1970

OTHER BOOKS CONNECTED
WITH THE SERIES

The Chalet Book for Girls – 1947
Second Chalet Book for Girls – 1948
Third Chalet Book for Girls – 1949
(TOM TACKLES THE CHALET
SCHOOL was serialised in the
second and third books.)

The Chalet Girls' Cookbook – 1953

A book about Elinor Brent-Dyer and
the Chalet School series – BEHIND
THE CHALET SCHOOL by Helen
McClelland – was published in 1981
by New Horizon, and is still available
from public libraries in most parts of
the country.

JOEY'S CONVICT

Even today, if someone says, "What price convicts?" to Jo Bettany and looks at her in a certain way, she goes scarlet.

This is the reason why.

Jo, aged fifteen, had come to England from her school in the Tirol to spend Easter with the school's senior mistress, Mollie Maynard. Miss Maynard had been with the Chalet School from its first term, and she and Jo, and Jo's sister Madge, who had begun the school, were all good friends. Madge had married Dr James Russell in the previous summer and had gone with him to the Sonnalpe, where he was running a sanatorium with the assistance of two or three other young doctors, among them Dr John Maynard, Mollie Maynard's twin brother. Jo knew Dr Jack, as the school called him, very well indeed. The eldest of the Maynard family, Captain Robert Maynard of the Hampshire Regiment, she had not met. For one thing, he was married, and he and his wife lived in London most of the time with their precious only son, Rolf. For another, the regiment had been stationed in the north during the previous eighteen months and he naturally spent his leaves with his wife and boy. Jo had had no chance to know him.

Mrs Maynard, a charming grey-haired lady in her sixties, looked up from her letters one morning with a beaming smile. "This is from Bob," she announced. "He's got an unexpected weekend, and is coming here, as Lydia and Rolf are in Cannes."

"Oh, good!" cried Mollie, who was very fond of her elder brother. "It's ages since we saw Bob – and Joey and Co will get to know him," she added with a twinkle at Jo, Jo's little adopted sister, Robin Humphries and Jo's friend Grizel Cochrane, who had also come to Pretty Maids for the holidays.

"Good-oh!" remarked Jo, helping herself to marmalade – they were at breakfast. "I'd like to know the Captain. He's years older than you, isn't he, Maynie?"

Mollie Maynard nodded. "Nearly eleven years older. When I was a small girl I always regarded him as a kind of uncle; but he's a dear. You'll like him, you three! Bob says that he won't be here till late on Friday, so you folk won't see him till Saturday."

"Can't we sit up for him?" asked Jo coaxingly.

"Mother wouldn't hear of it, as you very well know. No, my child, bed for you at nine as usual. Bob won't arrive much before eleven, if then." Then she changed the subject, and no more was said.

On the Thursday afternoon they had a visitor to tea, a middle-aged lady who, to quote Mollie Maynard, was "the worst old gossip in the county and a vicious old scaremonger into the bargain". Miss Maynard had taken Grizel and the Robin for a walk to the village, where they had dropped in at the Rectory for tea. Jo,

bothered with twinges of toothache all the previous night, had been sternly bidden to stay in
the house; on the morrow Miss Maynard would
take her to Portsmouth to visit the dentist. Jo
had spent her afternoon on the drawing room
sofa, and was feeling so much better for a long
nap that she was enjoying a cosy tea with Mrs
Maynard when Miss East was announced.

She came bustling in – a plump, short
creature, with wide blue eyes, a small, round
mouth and a somewhat foolish expression on
her face. On this occasion, however, she had
no sooner sat down and loosened her coat than
she plunged headlong into the latest alarm.

"Oh, dear Mrs Maynard, *have* you heard
the *awful* news?"

Mrs Maynard passed her a cup of tea.
"I do hope that is as you like it, Miss
East. Awful news? No; I can't say I've heard
any news that is especially awful. My eldest
boy is coming home tomorrow for the weekend;
and that's the greatest piece of news I've heard
lately. You remember Bob, don't you?" As she
said later, she didn't want Miss East to come
out with anything hair-raising before Jo, who
was sitting there, her ears literally waggling
with curiosity!

Miss East was not to be deterred, however.
"Oh? I didn't know," she said vaguely; then
went on with her subject: "I wonder you haven't
heard of it. Of course, it only happened this
morning; but it was given out over the radio on
the one o'clock news. A convict has escaped from
Portland! Isn't it dreadful? They say he is thought
to be coming in this direction – trying to get away
into the Forest, I suppose, and escape that way.
But isn't it *awful*? Why, he may break into our
houses and murder us all in our beds!"

"Oh, I don't expect so," said Mrs Maynard
soothingly. "Joey, run along to the kitchen, dear,

and ask Cook for some more hot cakes. I'm afraid these are cold now."

Joey took the muffin-dish and departed reluctantly. She was a young woman of vivid imagination and she was dying to hear more about the escaped convict. But by the time Jo returned to the drawing room, Mrs Maynard had managed to change the subject, and Miss East was in full cry after the iniquities of the Rector's wife, who had asked her to decorate the window sills of the church for Easter and given the font to Miss East's most deadly rival.

This topic lasted the lady through the remainder of tea, and Miss East departed shortly afterwards. Mrs Maynard warned Jo to say nothing about the convict before little Robin, who was a delicate child. The promise was given and Mrs Maynard went off to see to some other matters, quite satisfied.

Left alone, Jo finished up her letter and dropped it into the postbag, which one of the gardeners who lived in the village was to collect. Then the others came in, and over a riotous game of consequences she forgot Miss East and all her works. Indeed, it was not until she was snug in bed that the memory of the escaped convict came back to her. The dash of vicious spring rain against her window panes made her wonder where he was, and if he were out in the storm. Then she turned over and fell asleep.

Next day there was little time to think of convicts or anything else, for they had to have early breakfast in order to catch the train to Portsmouth, where Joey was to undergo her ordeal with the dentist. Sensitive and highly-strung, she always dreaded such visits, and she had very little to say for herself during breakfast and the journey, which lasted about an hour. Miss Maynard had brought her alone, leaving the others to spend the day at Pretty Maids.

The ordeal was bad enough, for the dentist discovered a hole in the tooth which had ached, and drilled it well and truly. There were two others needing attention, and by the time he had finished with her, Jo felt rather as if she had been a convict herself, condemned to a most unpleasant sentence. However, he finished with her at long last, and arranged for a further visit the following week.

"What would you like to do now?" asked Mollie Maynard as they descended the steps of his house. "What about coffee at Bobby's?"

"Good egg!" said Jo, who was still rather white after her trials. "And then, Maynie, what about going to that second-hand bookshop in Marmion Road? I'd like to see if I could get any more *Elsie* books."

"Very well," agreed Miss Maynard. "Only remember, Jo, you can't fill *all* your cases with books. You've got seven or eight already."

"Yes; but the *Elsie* books are thin. They don't take up much room," coaxed Jo. "Besides, Grizel says she'll take one or two for me."

"Oh, very well then. Come along and we'll have our coffee first!"

Coffee was a success, and Mollie Maynard was glad to see the faint colour coming to Jo's cheeks as she drank it.

"You look a little less like a scarecrow now," she said, as they turned down Marmion Road. "Really, Jo, when you go white, what with your black eyes and that black fringe of yours, you look a perfect sight!"

"I can't help the colour of my eyes and hair!" retorted Jo with spirit. Then she added wickedly, "Let's get some rouge and I'll do my cheeks, shall I? Then you won't need to be afraid people will think you are walking round with a dying duck."

"Just let me catch you doing it," was all the reply she got, and she chuckled.

The bookshop turned up trumps. Jo came away triumphant with *Christmas with Grandma Elsie* and a *Dimsie* book into the bargain.

"Some day," she informed Miss Maynard, as the train crawled up the valley, "I shall write school stories myself."

"I thought you meant to write historical novels?"

"So I do; but school stories will make a

nice change. I do love *Dimsie* and I've never read this one. Nor the *Elsie*, either. It hasn't been *all* waste today!"

"It was none of it waste," said Miss Maynard tartly. "Really, Jo, you are a perfect baby about going to the dentist."

"Well, he hurts so," complained Jo.

"I should say toothache on and off for days was far worse. Now be quiet and look at your books. I want to glance at mine." For Mollie had fallen in the bookshop, too, and bought a copy of a book she had long wanted.

Jo was quite agreeable, and for the next half hour there was silence in their compartment while Miss Maynard began her novel, and Jo herself was buried in *Christmas with Grandma*

Elsie.

When they got back to Pretty Maids, it was time for tea – they had had lunch in Portsmouth and gone for a blow in Southsea before catching the train back. After tea, Mrs Maynard sent the girls out to gather flowers to take on the morrow to the church, so they missed the six o'clock news. They also missed the arrival of a telegram.

"Shall we tell the girls?" asked Mrs Maynard of her daughter.

"No; they can see the pair of them at breakfast tomorrow," said Mollie decidedly. "I want Jo to get to bed early tonight. A visit to the dentist always tries her. She was as white as chalk when he'd done with her. By the by, I must tell you what the monkey suggested to me!" And with many giggles she told of Jo's plan for rouge.

Mrs Maynard chuckled too. "The imp!" she said comfortably. "However, that Matron of yours would soon find out if she tried it on at school; and her sister will see to it that she doesn't play pranks of that kind at home. Well, I suppose we'd better see to setting the Bachelor's room to rights. I'll just tell Saunders to have supper ready for the girls at half past seven, and then we can see to it ourselves."

Jo was quite ready to go to bed at half past eight, and Grizel also made no demur. She was feeling stiff after her ride that morning, and was, on the whole, quite pleased to lie down. Joey made one stipulation. She would go to bed without a fuss if she might read for a while. She argued that it was beyond human nature to expect her to have two new books and leave them alone till the morning.

Mrs Maynard, who was easy-going as a rule, laughed, and told her she might read till the clock struck nine. Then she must put her book away, turn out her light, and go to sleep.

"All right," agreed Jo, feeling that half a loaf was better than no bread. She was well on in the *Elsie* book, and longing to know what happened next. A rapid reader, she felt that she could get through a good deal before nine.

It is to be feared that her toilette was distinctly sketchy. She tossed off her clothes, wiped her face over with her facecloth, and dried soapy hands on her towel. Then she dropped on her knees at the bedside, said her prayers, and was into bed before Grizel had finished brushing out her lengthy locks. Their rooms communicated, and the door was open, so Grizel, peeping in as she plaited her hair for the night, commented enviously on Jo's luck in having short hair which had neither curls nor wave in it.

"If you had to get through the tangles *I* have to, you wouldn't be so quick," she said. "I say, Jo, I think I'll cut a fringe like yours! It would save me so much, anyhow."

"Don't!" advised Jo. "It wouldn't suit you at all. You'd look a most ghastly freak, just as I should if I hadn't one!" And she pushed back the heavy fringe to show a high, wide forehead.

"Mercy!" cried Grizel. "Jo, you *do* look awful – all face!"

"E-zackly! Now go away and let me get on with this priceless book."

"I can't think how you can waste your time over those Victorian horrors," declared Grizel, retreating into her own room. "All goody-goody and pi! Some folk are fond of a treat!"

Jo, however, was already fathoms deep in her book and made no reply, so Grizel finished undressing, got into bed, and after a glance at her own book, decided that she felt sleepy, switched off the light, and fell asleep. As for the Robin, she had a little bed in Miss

Maynard's room, which was on the other side of Joey's, and had been put to bed at half past six as usual.

Jo read and read until the solemn booming of the stable clock reminded her of her promise. Very reluctantly she scrambled through the last paragraphs of the chapter which tells how Lulu Raymond captures burglars by locking them into the strong room, shut her book, switched off her light, and then snuggled under the blankets. It was a chilly night, and the wind coming in at the open window was sharp, though she had been far too interested in her story to heed it till now.

Unlike Grizel, she was not drowsy, and she lay for some time thinking about what she had read. It brought back Miss East's tale to her mind, and she wondered where the escaped convict was now.

"If he came here we could catch him like Lulu caught her burglars," she thought with great lack of grammar. "There isn't a strong room, but the little cloakroom behind the stairs would do just as well. Nobody could get out of the window — even *I* got stuck the day I tried. And there's a jolly good bolt on the door. What a scream it would be! Wish he'd come and I could be the one to catch him. That would be something to talk about at school. *And* it might come in useful when I began to write school stories."

This sort of thinking was no help towards sleep. Jo lay wide awake in the dark. She heard the booming of the stable clock striking ten. Half an hour later, there were steps on the stairs. Just outside her door they paused, and she heard low voices.

"I don't think I'd go in, Mollie. Jo may wake, and she looked very washed out tonight, I thought."

"That was the dentist. Jo always reacts badly to such things. Don't worry, Mother.

She really is pounds stronger than she was.
Probably a good night's rest will set her right. I
won't go in if you think it better not. There isn't
a sound coming from her. I expect she's been
asleep this last hour or more."

Jo knew that she ought to let them know
she was awake, but by this time she really was
growing drowsy, and it was too much trouble
to rouse herself sufficiently to call out. Then
she heard the Squire coming, and a low mutter
from him which was quite indistinguishable. Mrs
Maynard replied.

"Oh, I think not, dear. They must have
been held up somewhere. Anyhow, it's almost
eleven. They'll be all right. Goodnight, Mollie.
Get to bed as soon as you can, dear."

"Yes. Goodnight, Mother. Goodnight,
Daddy!"

Footsteps passed on; doors closed quietly.
Jo was fast asleep.

It was a couple of hours later that she
suddenly roused up. As always, she woke
instantly, with no drowsiness to shake off. The
Easter moon was full, and its light, streaming
straight in at her window, was so brilliant, that
for a moment she fancied it was morning. Then
she heard the sonorous chime of the stable clock,
and counted one stroke. It was one o'clock and
a glorious night. Jo got out of bed quietly, went
to the window, and leaned out. The white light
of the moon poured over the great lawn, where
the shadows from trees and bushes were etched
with sharp black lines across the grass. The
wind had died down and the sky was ablaze
with stars. A shrill "Tu-u-u-who-o-o!" rang out
startlingly near at hand. Then, unmistakably,
there was the crunch-crunch of steps on the
gravel of the broad drive, and Joey, staring as
if her eyes would fall out of her head, beheld
a tall, manly figure coming slowly and wearily

up to the house.

Later, when it was all over, Jo was brought
to admit that what she ought to have done was
to go and call one of the grown-ups. Actually,
she did nothing of the kind. For a moment or
two she stood rooted to the spot. Then, with a low
chuckle, she slipped noiselessly to the bedside,
grabbed her dark blue dressing gown and pulled
it on, poked her feet into her matching slippers,
and stole quietly out of the room and downstairs.

She went into the morning room, which
had French windows reaching from the ceiling
to the floor, and looked out. The next moment
her heart gave a great thud, for at precisely
the same instant the intruder looked in! The
pair stood staring at each other for seconds.
Then Jo grasped at her self-possession. Swiftly,
a glorious plan shot through her head, and she
acted at once. Softly undoing the bolts of one
window, she opened it a crack.

"Come in," she whispered. "Don't make a
noise or you'll disturb the house."

Looking somewhat dazed, the newcomer did
as he was desired. Jo drew him in, realising as
she gripped his arm that he was soaking wet.

"Follow me," she whispered. "Go on your
toes. There are only rugs in the hall. I'll take
you to the kitchen. There's sure to be a bit of
fire left in the grate and I can get you a hot
drink. You *are* wet! What on earth have you
been doing?"

"Lost my way through that spinney," replied
her guest in a stage whisper. "Cocky said it was
a short cut, but it's the longest short cut ever I
met!"

By this time they had reached the hall,
and Jo put a finger on her lips. "Don't talk,"
she whispered. "Just follow me, and I'll see to
you."

Jo led the way through the hall. The

moonlight streaming in through the great staircase window gave them light enough to see their way, and in any case Jo was not startling the household by switching on any lights. Past the staircase they went, and down a little corridor shrouded in gloom, which was not reached by the moonlight. Jo stopped at a door and opened it. A faint glimmer showed through a small window in the opposite wall. She turned to the man.

"Will you go ahead, please? I must hold the door."

It was no time to argue. He did as he was told. The next moment, as he stumbled forward, the door was shut on him, and he heard the unmistakable sound of a shot bolt. He whirled round, and that was his undoing, for he got mixed up in some sort of netting, and came to the ground. Then he was aware that his hostess was addressing him through the door.

"You can stay there till the morning. I'm not going to disturb everyone and scare the Robin out of ten year's growth – which is what would happen if I did. She knows nothing about you, and I won't have her frightened. In the morning, we'll send for the police. Till then, you can settle yourself. You can't break the door down – it's too strong. And since *I* couldn't get through that window, you can't. So you can just make the best of it! Goodnight!"

He could hear no sounds, but as she stopped speaking, he concluded she had gone. For a few minutes he was so furious at being treated like this that he could only swear inarticulately to himself. Then the humour of the whole thing dawned upon him, and he gave way to a series of chuckles. He was very tired, however, and wet through, as he had stumbled into a shallow pond in the course of his wanderings. His eyes grew accustomed to the gloom, and he saw that he was in a cloakroom of sorts. There were coats and a big tartan cape hanging on the pegs. A couple of travelling rugs were folded neatly on a locker that ran down one wall, and when he had lit his lighter and peeped in, he found others. He decided to do as he had been told. In less time than it takes to tell he had tossed off his wet clothes, rubbed himself down with an old towel he found hanging in a corner — and which, had he known it, was used to wipe the dog's paws when they were muddy — put on one of the coats, rolled up another for a pillow, spread one travelling rug under him, and two more on top, and was soon sleeping as sweetly as most of the rest of the household were.

Upstairs, in her own comfortable bed, Joey was sobbing to herself, partly with reaction, partly because she felt that she was taking a fellow being's freedom away. However, she was really too worn out with excitement to cry long, and before long, she, too, was sleeping.

The next shock came early in the morning when the housemaid went to the cloakroom to put away her master's garden hat, which she had picked up from an old dower chest in the hall. Her wild yell when she unbolted the door and saw a strange man lying fast asleep on the locker roused most people very effectually.

What a commotion there was! Jo woke up in the middle of it, lay for a minute wondering what it was all about, suddenly remembered her night's adventure, and without stopping to don either dressing gown or slippers, tore off downstairs just in time to see Miss Maynard, who was very decorously in *hers*, caught in the captive's arms and hugged. What is more, she not only made no effort to get away, but flung her arms round his neck and kissed him rapturously, crying, "Oh, Ralph! We thought you and Bob couldn't arrive till later this morning! How *did*

you get in?"

Explanations in full came later on when everyone was properly clad and they were sitting down to breakfast. Before that, though, Miss Maynard had had an explanation all to herself, and took a malicious joy in grabbing Jo, hauling her up before the stranger, who was now shaved, washed, and clad in some spare garments of Dr Jack's, and saying sweetly, "Joey, I must introduce you to my future husband, Mr Ralph Arden. Thank you *so* much for the hospitality you showed him last night!"

Jo blushed to the roots of her hair, and did not know which way to look. However, Mr Ralph Arden showed no resentment. Instead, he heartily shook hands with her, saying, "Well, it was rather a rough welcome, but I don't mind as it made Mollie tell me something I've been wanting to know this last ten months. Let's forget it!"

However, when breakfast brought explanations, Mrs Maynard cried out in dismay. "Oh, my dear! The man was caught *yesterday after-noon.* The news was broadcast at six o'clock. I quite forgot you wouldn't know."

When it was all straightened out, Joey learned that Mr Arden was a friend of Captain Bob's – *he* nearly laughed himself sick over the story when he arrived shortly before ten and heard the tale

– who was first officer aboard a liner running between Southampton and Auckland, N.Z. The pair had met in Southampton at six the previous night, where Captain Bob was held up through having to see off the daughter of a fellow officer who was going to join her mother in Egypt. He had invited Mr Arden to accompany him down to Pretty Maids, and asked him to go on. He had also given his friend a description of a so-called short cut through the spinney adjoining the garden. Unfortunately, Mr Arden lost his way, and instead of arriving about eleven as they had expected, he had been two hours late, with the result which has been described.

The horrified Jo learnt also that in the short time before breakfast he had persuaded Miss Maynard to say that she would marry him when the summer holidays came, and go to out Auckland to make their home there. Grizel and Robin joined in her outcry at this news.

"What's the school going to do without you?" demanded the former.

"Get someone else," replied Mr Arden. "I'm giving her back to you for one more term, but after that, she belongs to me. However," he added, "you can all three be our bridesmaids – that is if Jo can bring herself to 'bridesmaid' someone she thought was a convict."

Jo blushed again. "Oh, you— you—!" she cried, then turned and fled, followed by the laughter of everyone else.

THE CHALET SCHOOL ON THE MOVE

LOCATIONS·2

THE SONNALPE - GUERNSEY - ARMISHIRE - ST BRIAVEL'S ISLAND

The Chalet School's happy years in Tirol come to a dramatic end with the Nazi annexation of Austria. For a brief interval the school finds refuge in an empty hotel on the Sonnalpe, named Der Edel Ritter (*The Chalet School in Exile*). And the Sonnalpe belongs to the category of places which blend real life and imagination.

Never again, after the stories move from "Briesau-am-Tiernsee" is it possible to state with the same assurance exactly where the school itself is situated.

Take the house known as Sarres, which becomes the school's temporary home in Guernsey, their first stop after leaving the Tirol. Minute details are available about the colour-wash on the walls, the paintwork in deep soft green, the plain net curtains "that had come from Tirol", and the polished, gleaming floors. The garden, restored after "years of neglect", is also described. But at no point are we told the exact situation of Sarres; only that the house, as Madge informs Joey – is: ". . . not far from Jerbourg where they intend to have the sanatorium." Jerbourg is of course a real place, but the precise location of the Chalet School is never established.

Nor is it possible, when the school moves on to "Armishire", to discover exactly where "Plas Howell", their new home, is situated. The books make clear that Armiford is Hereford and that Howell Village lies in the attractively named Golden Valley, about fourteen miles from Armiford/Hereford. In other words, in exactly the same district, towards the

Joey preparing for the escape into Switzerland

TH CHALET SCHOOL IN EXILE

ELINOR M. BRENT-DYER

Black Mountains and "on the English side of the Welsh border", as the real-life village of Peterchurch – a place Elinor had visited regularly in term-time during the four and a half years she was working as a daily governess. Not being a driver, she had always travelled by bus, and there is undoubtedly a remarkable likeness between the real-life journey from Peterchurch to Hereford and the journey, so often described in the stories, from Howell to Armiford. It seems likely that Howell Village was somewhere near to Peterchurch – or possibly to Vowchurch, the next village along the Golden Valley.

Elinor is lavish with details about Plas Howell itself, and pours out long and affectionate descriptions in most of the Armishire books.

Plas Howell obviously merits the description "a great mansion", which is often bestowed on it. In fact it sounds rather on the grand side to make really comfortable premises for a school, even one so relatively well-behaved as the Chalet School. One can understand Miss Annersley's reaction on her first visit to Plas Howell, when she sees ". . . the noble room with its built-in shelves laden with books, its comfortable saddle-bag chairs and sofa, its Chinese carpet in glowing blues and oranges", which is apparently to be her official headmistress's study, and asks doubtfully: "Are you sure this is the room Mr Howell meant, Jo?"

But all round, Plas Howell had much to recommend it. As the headmistress had noted on another occasion, there was plenty of room for the girls, the air was glorious, the grounds lovely, and the meadowland near the gates ideal for playing-fields. Altogether it must have been a considerable blow when "trouble with the drains" was diagnosed, and the Chalet School, after about eight happy years at Plas Howell, was forced to move elsewhere.

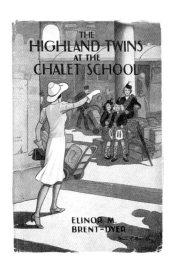

The next move takes the school to the "Island of St Briavel". Here for the first time in the series, the setting is entirely imaginary: there *is* a real place called St Briavels, but this lies between Monmouth and Chepstow, not far from Tintern, and it is definitely not an island. The stories provide various descriptions of the fictional St Briavel's, and two in particular are interesting because they appear to contradict each other. One states it to be "an island – in the Irish Sea off Wales"; the other, "an island off the coast of *South* Wales" – the Irish Sea lying of course off the west coast of Wales!

The island setting gives the school plenty of scope for new activities – rowing and bird-watching and so on – as well as for continuing with established pastimes like gardening and tennis. And Elinor is able to use the natural hazards of island life, among them tides, mists, and rock scrambling, to provide a number of exciting adventures.

As regards the house on St Briavel's, this was known simply as the Big House. It was "a square-built house, with walls that had been whitewashed from time to time". All the same, the Big House had its own kind of style, being especially well endowed with windows: at one side of "the deeply-recessed front door [there were] three wide bow windows"; on the other, "three sets of French windows"; and above them, "two rows of flat Georgian windows with small panes". The spacious grounds included not only lawns, flower borders and shrubberies, but a couple of tennis courts and an orchard. Once again the Chalet School had fallen on its feet.

For seven terms the Chalet School remains on St Briavel's. Then, some two and a half years after their arrival on the island, the final move takes place, this time to the Bernese Oberland.

A CHALET SCHOOL
CROSSWORD

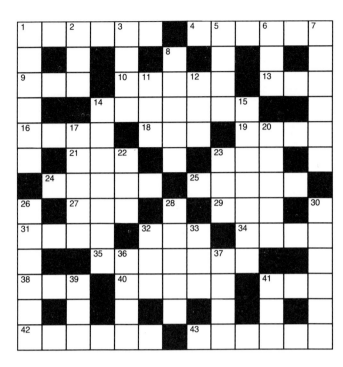

CLUES ACROSS

1. Emerence Hope's greatest friend
4. Prepared for a Staff Meeting by the Secretary in consultation with the Head
9. River which runs through Spärtz
10. Weather that caused a "famine" on the Görnetz Platz
13. Simone de Bersac, ——Lecoutier
14. A name that is mentioned in every Chalet School book
16. —— Ancockzy, later von Rothenfels
18. The home of what upset the "midnight" in the orchard
19. It is wrong to —— a duty!
21. The form in which metal is dug out of the earth
23. What Miss Nightingale's close friends may have called her
24. Mentioned in almost all the Chalet School books. She entered a convent.
25. What each Head of the Chalet School was determined to suppress
27. When the ice melted, the water —— away
29. English for 22 Down
31. Herr Ernst von ——hardt taught music to Nina Rutherford
32. Often used for cooking but now seldom for lighting
34. A ditch or bank
35. Homeland of Mary Shaw, Elma Conroy and Evadne Lannis
38. It was a tradition of the Chalet School to be kind and helpful to —— girls
40. She walked in her sleep and Joey fainted at the sight
41. She said that Daniel bit the lions!
42. She scorned all who were not *hochgeboren*.
43. The Mistress who refused to go to the Oberland.

CLUES DOWN

1. Jo Scott's mother
2. Present tense of 27 across
3. Puss undertook that his master (Blossom Willoughby) should k this monster
5. Plas ——————.
6. One of those who looked after and "bossed" Lady Russell wh Kevin and Kester were born
7. A royal maid who dressed Joey
8. Miss Burnett's sister
11. Women's service in the War
12. Sounds like a horse, but no!
14. Measles worked her cure.
15. She presented a fountain pen to the Bishop
17. Miss Ferrars shared the geography teaching with Miss ——
20. What Gay borrowed when she ran away
22. German for 29 across
23. Same as 23 across
26. Hilary ——————.
28. The youngest pupil at first
30. Sharper
32. What Bill hurt in a car crash (in reverse).
33. Part of a Brownie Pack
36. Inter V saw suits of armour or coats of —— at Solothurn
37. The kind that holds honey has six sides
39. What came to Lower IV after playing "Impertinent Questions
41. Minette

EXTRA QUESTIONS
From which Chalet School books we each of the following clues taken:
18 and 41 Across
7, 15 and 36 Down

JOSEPHINE MARY BETTANY

(known as Jo, or Joey) – later Mrs Jack MAYNARD

Jo becomes the Chalet School's first pupil, and she is unquestionably the most important character in the series. In the opening story she is a lively twelve-year-old with "at least five times as much spirit as strength", whose health at this point often gives cause for anxiety; and it is partly in order that her younger sister may benefit from mountain air that Madge chooses for her school a location three thousand feet above sea level.

In the "dry, life-giving air of the Tirolean alps" Joey's health improves rapidly. And although her propensity for launching into hazardous escapades involves her in a couple of dramatic illnesses, plus a handful of lesser ones, she eventually grows up to become, if not exactly robust, most certainly resilient.

As a schoolgirl, Jo is portrayed with quite a realistic mixture of good qualities and faults. Maybe she does have an extra lavish helping of gifts – among them, a sensitive imagination, great promise as a writer, a beautiful singing voice, and of course a warm heart and a charismatic personality. On the other hand, she is capable of being moody, is often impatient and at times sarcastic, even snappy when provoked. Into the bargain she is extremely untidy, and impulsive to the point of rashness. It all adds up to a convincing and attractive presentation which, in the early books, is always seasoned with a touch of humour.

Through most of her schooldays Joey shows a marked resistance to the idea of growing up; she even stages an outright protest when told

she has been appointed as the Chalet School's head girl. But during her final year her attitude begins to change a little. Then, later on, the harrowing experiences she endures during – and before – the escape from Austria, help to speed the maturing process. And despite her many declarations about remaining the family's permanent maiden aunt, Joey, by the time she is twenty, has married Jack Maynard, one of the doctors at the sanatorium on the Sonnalpe.

A year or so later her family is inaugurated – in characteristically startling fashion – by the arrival of triplet daughters. The Maynards are to be a large family: the total by the forty-eighth book of the series has reached eleven – six girls and five boys – and Joey is even threatening, perhaps not altogether seriously, to top up with quadruplets! Nevertheless, the demands of family life are not allowed to engulf Jo's irrepressibly youthful spirits. She insists that she will always remain a Chalet girl at heart, even when she's "a great-grandmother in a bath chair". And in addition to her duties as mother of eleven and joint guardian with her husband to several wards, she finds time to be a highly successful writer. Not to mention that she continues to play the roles of counsellor, comforter, champion "butter-in" and straightener-out of problems – both within and outside the Chalet School – to the very end of the series.

Jo Bettany/Maynard is unmistakably Elinor Brent-Dyer's own favourite among her enormous roll-call of Chalet School characters. Yet, interestingly, in a school where the majority of girls are pretty, and some outstandingly lovely, Jo is among the few with no claims to beauty. This Elinor makes clear from the first moment Jo appears on the scene. At this point, Jo's short black hair, cut with an uncompromisingly square fringe, was ". . . so straight as almost to be described as lank; her big black eyes made the intense whiteness of her face even more startling than it need have been, and her cheeks and temples were hollow with continual ill-health". And although before too long the "warm sun and clean mountain air" in the Tirol have "wiped out the unnatural pallor", with the result that Joey has "begun to lose her goblin-like appearance", we are still being told that "Pretty, she would never be". This, however, serves only to emphasise the close link between Jo and her creator; for Elinor herself was considered plain as a child, and it seems she was not altogether indifferent to her lack of beauty. And, in describing Jo's appearance (so well captured in Nina Brisley's illustrations for the early hardback editions) as "distinctive", or "full of character", but never in the least pretty, Elinor was almost certainly identifying with her best-loved heroine.

EARLY LIFE

Elinor's first home in Hereford (1933-8) – Stoneleigh, St James's Road

Not for Elinor Brent-Dyer the glorious mountains of the Tirol as a scenic backdrop to her childhood. The Chalet School's author was born and grew up in South Shields – an industrial town on Tyneside, which in those turn-of-the-century days was among the liveliest shipbuilding centres in the North-East but was hardly a glamorous place. Nor could 52 Winchester Street, the house where Elinor was born on 6th April 1894 and lived during the first nineteen years of her life, have been described as either high class or elegant. It was a respectable but very ordinary redbrick terraced house, dating from the 1870s. Nothing like the gracious homes inhabited by the Maynards and the Russells.

And it was not only in material circumstances that Elinor's childhood background differed from those of her fictional characters. In all her books Elinor shows a particular fondness for describing large happily united families, but she herself was one of only two children and she came from a broken home.

Her parents' marriage had been short-lived, and there are indications that a lack of harmony existed from quite early on. Certainly the couple were very different in both character and family background. Charles Dyer, Elinor's father, was an extrovert, and bohemian in tastes; his wife, Nelly, was by temperament and upbringing conventional. Nelly's family was well known in the north-east; Charles was a new arrival. He had retired early from the Royal Navy following a bout of ill health, and he had come to South Shields in the autumn of 1892 to work as a marine insurance surveyor.

The following spring Charles and Nelly were married; and the couple then set up house at 52 Winchester Street where Nelly had already been living since she was about six years old. Elinor was born a year later; and only fourteen months after that her brother, Henzell Watson Dyer, arrived on 25th June, 1895. His unusual first name is of Huguenot origin and it had been a favourite name with his mother's family, the Rutherfords, for well over a hundred years.

At this point the Winchester Street household included another important resident: Hannah Rutherford, Nelly Dyer's widowed mother. Hannah was a woman of strong character, and she not only lived in the house, she was its legal owner and had for many years been accustomed to acting as head of the family. For Charles Dyer the situation must have been difficult.

In any case, things were not quite as they

Winchester Street, South Shields, in the late fifties. Soon after this photograph was taken, most of the houses were demolished to make way for a housing estate. (Copyright © South Tyneside Central Library)

seemed at 52 Winchester Street. Outwardly the house appeared to contain a perfectly normal three-generations family: father, mother, two small children and a resident grandmother, with the occasional uncle or cousin staying for different lengths of time. But another person might by rights have expected to live with this household. Charles Dyer had been a widower at the time he married Elinor's mother and by his first marriage he had had a son, named Charles Arnold Lloyd Dyer. This little boy, barely five years old when his father married again, had spent the years after his mother's death in a pathetic kind of wandering passage between lodgings up and down the country, being for the most part left in the care of landladies. It is hard to think of any reason why poor Charles Arnold should not have come to live in South Shields with his father and stepmother once they had settled down after their marriage, for he had no other close relatives and there was ample room at 52 Winchester Street.

It seems that Nelly liked to keep things hidden, for in the same way that no one was aware of the existence of Charles Arnold, most people were not aware either of the true situation when, one day in 1897, Charles Dyer senior took his departure from Winchester Street never to return. Elinor's mother and grandmother seem to have taken extraordinary pains to disguise the breakdown of the marriage; and an impression spread around that Mrs Dyer was now a widow, having "lost her husband". And so in a way she had lost him, although Charles was not in fact to die until a further fourteen years after the legal separation took place.

At the time Elinor was barely three and Henzell not quite two. Unquestionably Mrs Dyer would not have informed her children when their father eventually set up house with another woman, by whom he later had a son and to whom he was to bequeath almost everything of which he died possessed.

Little wonder that Elinor grew up to be reticent where her personal life was concerned. A very early photograph of Elinor shows a very serious, rather wary and inward-looking little girl, with long straight fair hair, who appears to be about six years old. Not a very pretty little girl: the heavy features and the large nose characteristic of Elinor in later life are already foreshadowed. Nor does she look very happy. But perhaps it is not surprising that the small Elinor should appear somewhat mournful, for the people close to her did have an odd way of disappearing for one reason or another.

First it was her father. And although no one can say how much Elinor knew about him even

Elinor as a child, and in 1954 (copyright © Vivian's Studio, Hereford)

when she grew up, let alone how she felt, it could
be significant that, when she chose a new form
of surname to use as a writer, it was from her
father that she took the name Brent, adding it
with a hyphen to Dyer. That looks very much
like a gesture of solidarity.

Next it was her grandmother who vanished;
for in January 1901 Hannah Rutherford died,
leaving a wide gap in the Winchester Street
household where she had always wielded such
powerful influence. At this time Elinor was six
and three quarters and Henzell barely five and
a half; but, young as they were, it is unlikely
that this was their first experience of a death in
their immediate circle. The children of Elinor
and Henzell's generation would often hear of a
death in their own age group; for at that period
many serious and often fatal illnesses were still
common which are almost unknown today.

The third to go was her beloved brother,
Henzell, at the age of 17. With dramatic
suddenness, he was stricken with the painful illness cerebro-spinal meningitis and was instantly
taken into the local isolation hospital. Five days
later he was dead. This loss was to leave deep
and permanent effects on Elinor's personality:
Henzell had been her earliest companion and
the two had been thrown very much together
during those years when their mother, in her
attempt to build a wall of respectability round
the one-parent family, was discouraging contact
with the outside world. It had been Henzell
who joined in the imaginary games that Elinor
created from her earliest days; and it was to
Henzell that she had poured forth her first
stories. To the end of her life, fifty-seven years
after he died, Elinor would still be noting in her
diary that 25th June was "Henzell's birthday".
And although in later life she never talked about
her brother to anyone outside her immediate

circle, and seldom mentioned him even within it, it is clear that his memory always remained close to her.

PORTRAIT OF ELINOR M. BRENT-DYER 2

SCHOOL LIFE

School was to be a life-sentence in Elinor's case. For, if her own schooldays are added to the time she spent as student, pupil-teacher, teacher, and finally as headmistress of her own school, the impressive total amounts to almost half a century.

Her experience of schools was also wider and more varied than might be expected in view of the relatively narrow range of establishments portrayed in her books. She had become an "unqualified teacher" on her eighteenth birthday – 6th April 1912; and during the next thirty-six years she taught in a variety of both state and private schools, small and large, working with boys as well as girls and with mixed classes. She attended training college for two years to obtain a teaching qualification; taught, at different times, English, history, Latin, and class singing, and also coached hockey and folk-dancing. For a while she studied part-time at the Newcastle Conservatoire of Music, where she learnt piano, cello and singing. She worked for five years as a private governess; and finally became headmistress of a school she founded herself in Hereford.

This long procession of schools begins in about 1900 when Elinor first became a pupil at St Nicholas's School in South Shields. St Nicholas's was a select private school with around fifty pupils, including a number of small boys in the Kindergarten class (Elinor's little brother spent a couple of years there). It was run by two formidable ladies, the Misses Alice and Henrietta Stewart, and significantly the school was always known locally, not as St Nicholas's but as "The Misses Stewart's School". In their school a strong emphasis was laid on the paramount importance of good manners and ladylike behaviour, while the teaching was possibly on the old-fashioned side even for the times. From Elinor's point of view this was hardly the right balance: she was a clever child who could have benefitted from more high-powered academic teaching but it was not easy for her to assume a mantle of low-key refinement. She had inherited from her father a tendency to be outspoken, and an extrovert temperament, quite different from her mother's more conformist personality; by nature she was full of enthusiasm and exuberance, was considered boisterous in behaviour as a child, and throughout her life had a rather loud voice, a hearty laugh, and a considerable disregard of conventions in dress and manner. Decidedly not the qualities to make her a model pupil at the Misses Stewart's establishment.

Elinor's first experience of teaching was in a couple of the local Board Schools, as they were then known. Here she quickly gained the reputation for colourful eccentricity which was to follow her into her student days – for no obvious reason she used the name Patricia Maraquita while at the City of Leeds Training College – and right through her whole teaching career. This later on included several more local authority schools and the well-respected Boys' High School in South Shields, independent schools in Middlesex and Hampshire, and even a short spell filling in at The Misses Stewart's School.

Last of all, after moving to Hereford in the

1930s, she set up her own school, the Margaret Roper School (named after Sir Thomas More's accomplished daughter). This real-life school, which ran for ten years from September 1938, shared many ideals and customs with the fictional Chalet School, and it too had a strong, though non-denominational, religious tradition.

The Margaret Roper School was never to enjoy the phenomenal record of the Chalet School, although it was moderately successful for a number of years and undoubtedly filled a local need during the war. But Elinor, despite her gifts as a teacher, was not cut out to be a headmistress; and towards the end her interest in the real-life school was rapidly fading and becoming ever more fixed on the imaginary establishment.

All in all she was perhaps not really sorry in July 1948 when the Margaret Roper School finally closed its doors. Now at last she could give her undivided attention to the Chalet School.

Lichfield House, Hereford. Premises of the Margaret Roper School (1938-48) and Elinor's home until 1964. Below, pupils of the school

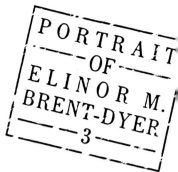

BOOK LIFE

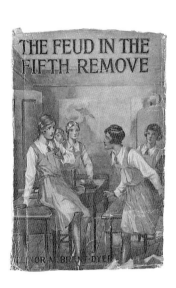

During the ten-year life of the Margaret Roper School Elinor had managed, in the midst of all her other commitments, to write and publish fourteen books. In the decade that followed, her output rose to the remarkable total of thirty-eight – sixteen of the books being completed within two years.

That tells much about the change in her circumstances. But it also confirms that Elinor's competence in the sheer mechanics of producing a book had been increasing steadily through the years. Not that her later books are superior in quality. On the contrary, most of her best stories belong to the early and middle years of her writing career. But undeniably she had in the course of time learnt many tricks of the trade.

At first, she did not enjoy quite the same precocious success as her Chalet School heroine, Jo Bettany, whose first book appears when she is only eighteen: Elinor was to be twenty-eight before *her* first book was accepted for publication.

This book, *Gerry Goes to School* (published by W. & R. Chambers in 1922, and a most important milestone in Elinor's career) was specially written for a little girl named Hazel Bainbridge, a gifted child actress to whom Elinor was devoted. Less than a year later *Gerry* had a sequel; and in the following year Elinor took a further step forward with *The Maids of La Rochelle*, the first of her Guernsey stories. But although the story marked another milestone, it was only a milestone. The really momentous turning point in Elinor's writing career was to

come with her visit to Austria in 1924.

Immediately on returning from the Tirol to her teaching post in Hampshire, Elinor got started on *The School at the Chalet*; and this book, which eventually would have fifty-eight successors, was published by W. & R. Chambers in October 1925: at its first appearance it was in a brown hardback edition, with a pictorial cover as well as a charming coloured dust-wrapper and four black and white illustrations by Nina K. Brisley (who was to provide illustrations for nearly half the series). The Chalet School was on the road.

From now onwards Elinor was to continue producing books, and at an increasing rate, until the end of her life (the last of the Chalet School series, *Prefects of the Chalet School*, was in fact published six months after she died).

Frontispiece and text illustration from *The School at the Chalet* (by Nina K. Brisley). The frontispiece shows Grizel Cochrane, the second illustration Simone Lecoutier

Altogether during the forty-seven years spanned by her writing career her output was more than a hundred published books; there were also the "missing" Chalet School stories (see *Questions* p. 94) and a number of unpublished manuscripts, including two collections of poems and a massive historical novel about Sir Thomas More and his family. Among the published books there are two series in addition to the Chalet School stories: "La Rochelle" (seven books) and "Chudleigh Hold" (three books), as well as several linked pairs of stories. There are fourteen books about schools other than the Chalet School, and one Girl Guide story; the remainder are family stories, adventure stories and historical tales.

All round not a bad achievement; especially bearing in mind that Elinor was obliged until she was fifty-four to continue working at least part-time as a teacher and could write only in the evenings or during the holidays.

But it all comes back to that holiday in Austria. For it was this which gave birth to the Chalet School. And beyond any possible question it was the Chalet School series that carried Elinor Brent-Dyer's name throughout Britain and into many far corners of the English-speaking world. Just as it is the Chalet School books that are still keeping her name alive today, more than sixty years on.

Elinor's total output numbered more than one hundred books. None are in print today save the Chalet School series

POSTSCRIPT

The end of the story

For a considerable period after her mother's death Elinor struggled to continue living in the enormous Victorian villa that had housed her school. Eventually, towards the end of 1964, friends succeeded in persuading her to sell up and move with them into a house at Redhill in

Surrey.

Her health was now beginning to fail. And it seems that for the first time Elinor's hitherto inexhaustible vitality and enthusiasm were also flagging. But she was to continue with the Chalet School books, five of which were produced during these last years at Redhill.

Her death, when it came on 20th September 1969, was quite sudden and peaceful.

Examples from Elinor's notebooks. She carefully counted every word she wrote

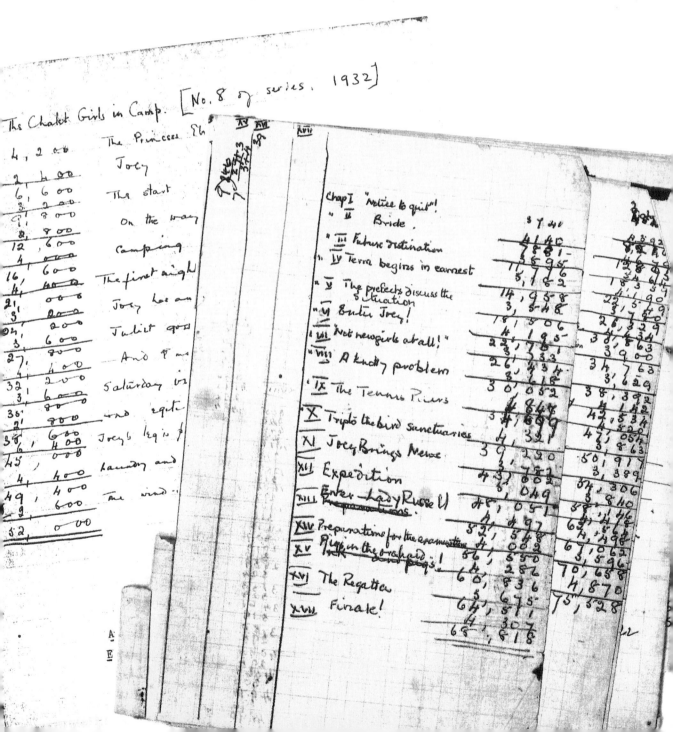

WELSEN – THE GÖRNETZ PLATZ

For most pupils of the Chalet School, the adventure in Switzerland begins only in the 30th book (*The Chalet School and Barbara*); but an advance party had already been launched into the Oberland a year earlier (see No. 26, *The Chalet School in the Oberland*).

The places named in the Swiss books are, as before, a mixture of the real and the imaginary. Basle, Zurich, Lucerne, Geneva, Montreux and Berne, for example, all figure in the stories at different points, and receive descriptions, often in some detail. And in answer to the question "How do we get there?", Miss Annersley makes a similarly detailed reply, depicting the transit by steamer and rail to Paris, then Berne and finally to Interlaken, whence they would take the mountain train up to the Platz". From this description, and others, it is possible to pinpoint the approximate location of Welsen and the Görnetz Platz – in the Mürren/Wengen/Lauterbrunnen area – but attempts to get any closer than this are defeated by Elinor's deliberate misplacement of fixed reference points. As a result, the Görnetz Platz, home to the Maynard family as well as the Chalet School and the sanatorium, must remain a place of the author's invention, not of reality, although it is none the less real to readers for all that.

WOOLLEN MEASLES

Matron Lloyd of the Chalet School was sitting
in her pretty room, frowning over her dormitory
lists, when there came a tap at the door. Matron
jerked up her head sharply with a flutter of
"angels' wings" from her cap, and called "Come
in!" The door opened, and a slim, dark-eyed girl
of sixteen entered.

"Please, Matron, Joey said I was to come
to you for my unpacking lists," she said in the
fluent French which was one of the three staple
languages of the Chalet School.

Matron nodded, and picked up a pile lying
at hand. "You are the last, Luigia. The others
have all got theirs – and here are yours," she
added, handing over three sheets. "You have
one lot in Middle House. The others are for
Junior. Do the Middles first, please. Most of
them are 'old' girls, but you have one new one –
an English child, Dorothea Buck. I sent her off
with Mary Shand, by the way. Off you go, now!
I'm busy. Go in by the side entrance, and you'll
find someone who can show you the run of the
house."

Luigia laughed. "And I shall be one of the first of our crowd to see it. We have all been so curious, Matron."

"I know that. Be off with you!" And Matron waved a brusque hand to the door.

Luigia bobbed the curtsy usually accorded to members of staff in this English school in a foreign land, and withdrew to go racing down the stairs, across the sunny garden which surrounded the Chalet School proper, and across the turf to where the new house rose in all its glory.

She entered by the side door, and found herself in a long, light corridor, with closed doors on either side. Rather uncertainly, she went along till she came to one door from which issued a steady buzz of chatter which told her that she had reached the common room. She turned the handle and walked in, nearly upsetting a short sturdy girl of fourteen or fifteen, whose most noticeable features were a short bush of yellow hair and a pair of enormous blue eyes.

"Oh, Corney, I am so sorry," said the Senior. "I hope I haven't hurt you or Evvy?"

Cornelia Flower felt her arms carefully. "Guess I'm still all here, thanks. Why've you come, Luigia?"

"Corney! How rude!" cried her companion, Evadne Lannis. "Jolly to see you, Luigia. Is this a visit of inspection, or what?"

"Unpacking," returned Luigia, holding up her lists.

"Oh! Who've you got? Let's see!" And the pair of them craned their necks to examine the top list.

"Garden Dorm," remarked Evadne. "H'm! Mary Shand – Hilda Bhaer – Berta Hamel – Dorothea Buck – who's she? Oh, the new girl, I guess."

"Another?" Cornelia sounded disgusted. "Why do they want to come *this* term? *Next's* the proper time! Have you seen her, Evvy?"

"With the plateful I've got already? I've had no time to go fagging after new kids," Evadne informed her. "Say, Luigia, did you know that us two and Lonny Barkocz and Maria Marani are Seniors here? Fact! And we aren't in dormies, either. Lonny and Maria share one room, and Corney and I another. And Jo, Marie, Frieda, and Simone are our prees, and they have a room each."

A gleam of mischief lit up Luigia's usually dreamy eyes. "What *was* Matey thinking about to put you two together?" she said.

Evadne drew herself up with a toss of the short fair curls that just touched her shoulders. "Guess we can behave as well as the next if we want to!" she retorted. "It was all very well having rags when we were only kids—"

"But now we're Seniors, we'll give you folk a shock," Cornelia concluded for her.

"If you do reform, you certainly will," Luigia assured her.

"Just you wait and see. Well, I suppose we'd better collect your little lambs. Half a mo!" And raising her normally pretty voice to a bellow that might have roused the envy of an old-time skipper rounding Cape Horn in a violent storm, Evadne yelled, "Silence!"

A brief hush ensued, as most folk turned to see what she wanted, and Luigia seized on it to read out the names of the girls on her list. Three girls detached themselves from various groups, one of them looking back to say imperatively, "Come on, Dorothea Buck; we've got to go and unpack."

A shy-looking child of thirteen or so who had been sitting on one of the wide window seats, gazing out at the garden with large dark eyes that saw very little, got to her feet and came to them, turning pink as she did so.

"This is Dorothea Buck," said the summoner, turning to Luigia, "Dorothea, this is one of the prefects, Luigia Meracini."

Luigia smiled at her, and spoke a few words of greeting in her prettily-accented English; then she led them out of the room and turned to the eldest of them with, "Hilda, I do not know the way, of course, so will you lead, please?"

Hilda, a quiet, rather colourless girl, nodded and smiled, and led the way up the stairs, along another wide corridor, and into a long, sunshiny room which was divided by rods and curtains into cubicles.

"This is Garden," she said. "Look at our pretty curtains, Luigia."

Luigia glanced round appreciatively. The curtains were of flower-besprinkled cretonne, and there was a stencilled border to match running under the dark-green picture rail which topped the paler-green walls, and matched the rest of the woodwork. Similar curtains drifted backwards and forwards at the open windows. Some of the cubicle curtains were drawn, and a low murmur of voices came from them; but some were flung over the seven-foot-high rails showing the small beds with counterpanes matching the general floral scheme. The whole effect was very light and fresh.

"It is very pretty," the prefect said. "Yes; I do like it. Now which are your cubicles, Hilda?"

Hilda consulted the list pinned on the notice board behind the door. "Seven, and nine, ten, and eleven," she said.

"Then let us begin. I have to go over to the Juniors when I have finished with you. Where are the carrying trays?"

"You can have mine – I've finished," said

a voice; and a small, very fair girl with startlingly black lashes and brows suddenly appeared, holding out a light wicker tray with a handle at each end. "Hello, Luigia. Paula's in the trunk room. She's been unpacking us – unless she's finished and gone elsewhere," she added.

"Thank you, Emmy," said Luigia, taking the tray and handing it to Hilda. "Here you are, Hilda. And there are two others over there. Now come along, all of you."

They left the dormitory and went to the far end of the corridor where there was a small square room in which trunks had been placed in serried ranks, one or two of them obviously unpacked, for they were piled up against the wall while the others stood near the door. Luigia called for keys and Hilda produced hers, and, when the trunk was unlocked, handed over the inventory which was pinned to the lid, and work began.

Luigia called out the articles from the list, while Hilda counted them and then laid them in her tray until it was full. Then she and Berta Hamel picked it up and went off with it to put the clothes away, while Luigia turned her attention to the new girl's belongings.

Now, though Luigia was a conscientious enough girl in many ways, she was an inveterate dreamer, which was the reason why Matron had chosen reasonably careful people for her list. Having seen Dorothea and Mary well started, the prefect leaned against the wall, staring dreamily out of the window at the beautiful Tiern See, loveliest of Tirolean lakes, which lay blue and sparkling in the spring sunlight. When Hilda and Berta returned, the prefect was still dreaming as she mechanically finished reading the list; and when Mary Shand arrived with Dorothea in tow she was still only half

awake and paid no attention to American Mary's
rather shocked comment of "No woollies, Doro!
Gee! Matey will have something to say! Luigia,
Doro hasn't a woollie to her name – undies, I
mean."

"Very well," said Luigia, not really taking
in one word of all this. "Finish with that trunk,
you two, and then I'll do Mary and Berta. And
do hurry! I've got to get over to Le Petit Chalet."

"Well, I've *told* her. I reckon it's no real
business of mine," thought Mary as she helped
the newly-christened "Doro" to empty the trunk,
carry off the loaded tray, and then put the things
neatly into her drawers. All the same, she spoke

her mind to her new acquaintance later on.
"Didn't you know we have to have three warm
woollen vests even this term? The summer's hot
enough, but we get some real freezing nights up
to the middle of May."

Doro said nothing. She was desperately shy,
and desperately homesick. An only child, living
in the heart of the country where she had had
a governess, she knew very little of other girls,
and Mary's offhand friendliness repelled her and
made her shrink into her shell. That young lady,
having done her full duty, said no more, and
soon forgot the whole thing.

For the next few days the sunny weather
continued, and Doro began very slowly to settle

down. So far as work was concerned, she found that she was well up to the standard of Lower Fourth where she had been placed. Miss Graham had grounded her thoroughly, and though at first she found some difficulty in working with nearly thirty other girls, she began to learn to manage. But it was a different thing when it came to out-of-school ploys. She had played a little tennis with her governess, but of cricket she knew nothing. At home, when lessons and walk were over, she had amused herself with story-books, sewing, and other quiet employments. Mrs Buck was a very frail woman, and the entire household had revolved round her.

Then the doctor had urged them to try the great sanatorium on the Sonnalpe for her; and when he had mentioned the Chalet School, only an hour and a half to two hours away, that had settled it. Thus Doro found herself in a place where she was expected to join in wild games of Rounders or Tag, or else go with the others for what they were pleased to call "a walk".

During the season when the Tiernsee district was filled with visitors the girls "croc-ed" through Briesau, the little village where the school stood, though they broke ranks once they were away from public gaze. Just at present the season had not begun. The mountain railway which brought tourists up from Spärtz, the tiny town at the foot of the mountain, would not be running for some time yet. Only one of the big hotels was open, and the girls took advantage of this to scatter in all directions, rambling along with their special chums in threes and fours, and even breaking into song on occasion. This was not what Doro called "a walk".

The others tried to draw her into their interests, for that was the tradition of the school; but she refused to be drawn. After a fortnight or so they gave it up. She was not neglected, but she stayed on the edge of their amusements.

Then came a spell of cold, rainy weather when the winds whirled through the valley, laden with the sharpness from the snows that still lingered on the mountain peaks, and the rain beat on steadily.

Matron, as head of the domestic staff, issued a ukase concerning woollies to her subordinates at St Agnes', as Le Petit Chalet was now called, and St Clare's, which was the new house. Matron Besly, new, young, and very full of her own dignity, merely put up a notice about it, while the other two went round the dormitories in the morning and saw to it that orders were obeyed.

Joey Bettany, head girl of the school, saw the notice, but concluded that Matron Besly had gone the rounds. As she herself was exempt from such supervision, and in any case had learned what to expect after living in the Tirol for some years, it never dawned on her that anyone in Matron's position could, as she said later, be such a ninny as to leave such a thing to a mere *notice*! None of the other three prefects saw any reason for troubling, either; and most of the "old" girls were only too glad to put on their warm clothes. Only Doro, unaccustomed to both the Tirol and school, never saw the notice, and shivered uncomplainingly in her thin cotton vests, wishing the summer heats would come. She went to bed night after night chilled and shivery. The natural result was that she caught a cold.

Matron Lloyd chanced to meet her in the corridor at St Clare's the next morning as she was going to her form room, just in time to hear her produce a most colossal sneeze. When she had finished – she sneezed at least nine times – the Chalet School's tyrant advanced on her, demanding, "What on earth have you been doing to catch such a cold? Come upstairs with me at once."

Terrified beyond measure, since she had been at school long enough now to have learned some of the legends that were rapidly growing round "Matey", as everyone, staff and girls alike, affectionately called her, Doro obeyed, and was soon established in Matey's own warm room, where she was given a couple of aspirins and a hot drink and then bundled up in a blanket and tucked up on Matey's bed, whereupon that lady herself went in search of Miss Wilson, Head of St Clare's.

"Bill" appeared shortly after Mittagessen, as Doro was learning to call the midday meal, picked up the patient in strong arms, and bore her off to the sanatorium at the far end of St Clare's, where she was put to bed with a hot bottle and a cup of good strong broth by Matron Besly, since Nurse, who was normally in charge, had ricked her ankle on the stairs that morning and was *hors de combat* at the moment.

On undressing the child, Matron, of course, found that she was not wearing wool as the notice had ordered, and gave free rein to a sharp tongue. Doro was feeling thoroughly poorly, and Matron's scolding brought back in full force the shyness which had been slowly evaporating during the last few days. The child lay tongue-tied and unable to explain that she had no woollen under-things for the very good reason that she was unable to wear wool next to her skin.

Matron Besly finished her remarks, went off to seek for woollies in the Garden dormitory, found none, and came back to demand to know the meaning of it. Doro remained dumb with fright, so Matron, after a final comment on the rudeness of some children, for once took the sensible course, went off to Matey, and returned

with one of the needed garments and a promise
that the Bucks should be asked to explain why
their daughter had not been properly provided.

Five days later, being certified as non-
infectious, she was allowed to get up; but
Matron supervised her dressing and saw to it
that she put on the warm vest. Doro was still
too nervous to explain, so she did as she was
told, well knowing that the day would be one
of torture to her, for the wool would tickle her
tiresomely fine skin almost beyond bearing.

She was allowed to join the rest for Kaffee
und Kuchen, which takes the place of tea in the
Tirol, and Mary Shand the sharp-eyed noticed
her squirmings at once.

"Say! Have you got fleas?" she demanded.

Doro was indignant enough at the accusation
to fire up. "Of course I haven't!"

"Then why are you hotching about like
that?" Mary wanted to know.

"It's this horrid woollen vest."

"Poor you!" observed Jeanne le Cadoulec,
a Breton girl. "But you must wear it while
this cold lasts, for Matey would never let you
off whatever our own idiot might do." By which
rude reference she meant Matron Besly.

"Try wearing it inside out tomorrow," coun-
selled someone else. "That may take the edge
off it a bit."

However, the next chapter in the story made
this unnecessary. Matron arrived at bedtime to
rub Doro's chest with camphorated oil, and was
horrified to find her patient's body covered with
a fine rash. She remembered the streaming cold,
put two and two together, and made a quite
possible four of them – only in this case it
turned out to be at least seven or eight.

With an exclamation of "*Measles*!" she
hurriedly wrapped up the startled Doro and
bundled her back to the San, where she put

her to bed. She then hastened back to forbid the members of Garden to leave their dormitory until given permission next morning.

Matey, duly apprised of what had happened, promised to ring up the Sonnalpe, where dwelt Mrs Russell, once Madge Bettany, and owner of the school, with her husband, Dr Russell, who with various other members of his staff overlooked the health of the girls. She was upset at the news Matron Besly hurled at her over the inter-house phone, for she had no wish for an epidemic so early in the term, especially as it would be a very short term in any case. She rang up Die Rosen, the Russells' pretty home, and broke the news to the doctor, who groaned loudly when he heard it.

"Measles! Are you sure? Has Jo been in it?"

"Not so far as I know," Matey replied. "No; when I come to think of it, the child was in the San until Kaffee und Kuchen, and Jo was over here till after eight o'clock. They had an extra science lesson with Miss Wilson, and there was a Prefects' meeting afterwards, so those four all stayed with us until after Abendessen, and Matron Besly seems to have found it out just before they went back to St Clare's."

"Well, keep them well away from the Middles, and tell Matron to send their Frühstück up to the dormitory, and not to let any of those Garden people mix with the others. If it *is* measles, they're the most likely ones to come down with it."

"Very well," agreed Matey. "And you'll come down in the morning?"

"As soon as I can. Keep out of it yourself, Matey. Nurse should be all right now. Is she back on duty?"

"Not till tomorrow, I believe. She will be then."

"Thank goodness for that! Oh, and send

Matron Besly some of that cooling mixture you have, and tell her to give the child a dose tonight and another in the morning." And he rang off.

So the not ungrateful Middles were kept strictly to quarters, though the Seniors, not having been near Doro, had Frühstück in the dining room and went over to lessons as usual.

The doctor arrived shortly after eleven, and went to see the patient, who had been kept in bed. Her cold was practically gone, but there was no doubt about the rash. She was covered with it. The doctor examined her carefully, and then stood up, a twinkle in his eyes.

"Well, Matron," he said, "I'm thankful to tell you that for once it's a false alarm."

"A false alarm! But look at the rash!" exclaimed Matron.

"That's not measles — which accounts for the disappearance of the cold and the lack of any temp. That's wool rash."

"*Wool* rash?"

"Yes. Tell me — Dorothea, isn't it? — have you been wearing wool next to your skin?"

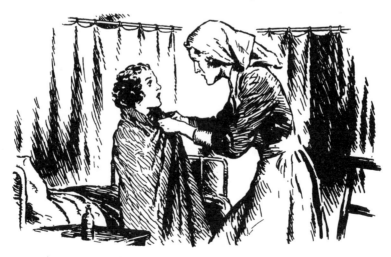

Matron replied for her. "Certainly she has — though only since yesterday. I found that she caught her cold through not obeying my notice and putting on a woollen vest. And—"

"That's it, then," he said, cutting short what looked like a lengthy diatribe. "Dorothea, do you ever wear wool at home?"

"No," said Doro shyly. "I – I can't. It's too scratchy."

"I thought so. You're one of those unlucky people who get wool rash if they wear wool next to their skin. But why didn't you tell Matron?"

Doro went red. "I – I couldn't."

"I'd like to know why not?" burst indignantly from Matron.

Luckily the doctor understood small girls. "I expect it was a bit hard when she is so very new," he said soothingly. "Well, Matron, I'll give you a lotion to soothe the irritation, and the rash will soon vanish. Don't put her into wool again – there shouldn't be any need of it, fortunately. That sun looks as though he has come to stay. Now I'll just take a dekko at those Middles to be safe, and then I'll mix you the lotion. When she's been dabbed with it she can get up. There's very little wrong with her."

He projected a smile at Doro as he departed, and that heroine contrived to give him one in return.

However, it was Nurse who appeared with the lotion, and Nurse's cheery talk soon took away the feeling of fright Matron roused in her. When she was finally dressed, and feeling more comfortable already, Doro was quite able to go to join the others, who were anxiously awaiting her to show her how grateful they were for their brief respite from lessons. Before another fortnight had ended she had forgotten most of her shyness, and, thanks in the main to what Jo Bettany described then and ever as "Woollen Measles", was soon well on the way to becoming a regular Chalet School girl.

QUESTIONS AND ANSWERS

Did the Chalet School ever exist in real life?
The stories have described the school so convincingly that readers often assumed the author had a real school in mind; a few simply took this for granted and wrote to ask the publishers for a prospectus! But in fact the Chalet School itself is entirely imaginary. However, its original location in the Tirol does exist, and the school's imagined position there can be pinpointed quite closely.

Were any of the characters in the stories real people? – or based on real people? – perhaps the author herself, her friends or relatives?
Most fictional characters do of course grow from a mixture of the author's imagination and experience; but it seems that none of the Chalet School characters is an exact portrait of any one real life person. And Elinor Brent-Dyer always denied that she had based any of them on herself or on people she knew. Nevertheless, there can be no question that a

great deal of Elinor herself went into her portrayal of Joey Bettany/Maynard. The two have so much in common, despite the obvious differences in their lifestyles and physical appearance, that it is clear Elinor must have identified strongly, if unconsciously, with Jo. A very old friend was convinced that "Joey was Elinor herself, as she would have liked to be". And there are traces of real people to be found in several characters. The Robin for example, appears to owe something to the child Hazel Bainbridge, for whom Elinor wrote her first published book, although Robin is not actually a portrait of Hazel. Elinor also had a misleading habit of giving her fictional characters the names of people she knew in real life. The most confusing example concerns Madge Russell: this, as every reader will know, is the married name of Madge Bettany who, in fiction, founds the Chalet School. But it was also the name of one of Elinor's real-life friends, to whom she dedicated three books – her Guernsey story *The Maids of La Rochelle*, and both the second

and third Chalet School books. Seeing this name printed in the dedications was, to me as a child, proof positive that the Madge of the stories really existed. However, no one has been able to trace any connection.

Are any of the places in the stories real?
Yes, many of them are real places, and some are a mixture of real and imaginary; but for more information on this matter see the section on *Locations* (p. 24).

Why does Mademoiselle change her name?
It has to be confessed right away that there is no absolutely definite answer to this question! In the first three books, Mademoiselle's surname is La Pâttre – two words, and spelt with an "A". In the fourth book, the name has become one word, but still spelt with an "A", viz.: Lapâttre. And through these four books her first name is Elise; at any

rate this is the name Madge uses, when addressing her in private. Then all of a sudden, in the fifth book, we find Mademoiselle has now become Lepâttre – one word, and spelt with an "E". And the next time a Christian name is mentioned she has become Thérèse. Moreover she continues to be Thérèse until the end. Now Elinor was unquestionably a rather forgetful and disorganised person. But it is hard to believe that, during a period of only four years, she could possibly have managed to forget the name she had given to one of her principal characters. Yet, if the change was not a mistake, what possible reason can Elinor have had for making it? No likely explanation comes to mind. And the mystery has never been solved. It does, however, seem that the discrepancy must have been pointed out to Elinor, for she stages a kind of salvage operation in *Jo to the Rescue*, the nineteenth book of the series; here, Simone introduces her daughter as "Thérèse Elise – after a cousin who died . . ." And full marks to Elinor for ingenuity, even if this still leaves unexplained the matter of La Pâttre/Lapâttre/Lepâttre.

Which of the Matrons is the real "Matey"? – sometimes she seems to be Lloyd, sometimes Gould, and at least once Rider . . .

This, which is similar to the previous question, has also caused endless confusion. But here it is possible to straighten things out by referring to the books – and keeping a cool head. And, weighing one thing with another, it can be established that the real "Matey", who first appears in the missing story that precedes *Head Girl of the Chalet School*, is quite definitely Matron Gwynneth Lloyd. For one thing, Matron Gould, who joins the school later and takes charge of the Juniors, "stood five foot eleven in her stockings", whereas "Matey" is small and wirey. Both Matrons, Lloyd and Gould, are mentioned by name in *Jo Returns to the Chalet School*, making clear that they are two different people. Then Matron Rider belongs originally to St Scholastika's School and joins the Chalet School staff only when the two schools merge. As to why the confusion happens, the answer must be the same as to the question above.

What is the best way to collect a complete set of the Chalet School books?

Armada has now published over three-quarters of the series in paperback and further titles are scheduled until 1993. All may not be currently available but a varying selection is kept in print, and with a bit of patience it should be possible to acquire all of them. At the moment, however, there are no plans to include in Armada the titles which do not deal directly with the Chalet School, for example *Jo to the Rescue* (a holiday story, set in Yorkshire). Anyone interested in reading this, or other stories which do not appear in Armada, or who would like to have some of the original hardbacks, should try searching at secondhand booksellers or in charity shops, where these books do turn up from time to time, although unfortunately their prices nowadays can sometimes be rather high. There is also a modern hardback edition of the first four stories, published in September 1988 by W. & R. Chambers Ltd; these have beautiful reproductions of the original dust-wrappers, and the books are currently available.

JOEY'S FAMILY

Joey confiscating Mario and Maria Balbini's catapult (*The New Chalet School*). Madge and the Robin are in the background

Just like a Charlotte Yonge family! – people in the Chalet School books often make this comment about the Maynards. And although today the comparison may not convey much to some readers, anyone familiar with the once-popular Victorian novelist, Charlotte Mary Yonge, will know exactly what to expect. The families in books by Miss Yonge seem always to include at least nine or ten children; quite frequently there are more, with pairs of twins being a common occurrence. Elinor is known to have admired Charlotte Yonge; and certainly her own stories include a striking number of large families, Joey's being of course the most numerous of all.

The odd thing is, so far as Joey is concerned, that she in her schooldays had frequently been heard proclaiming that marriage and children were not for her. She was going to be the delightful maiden aunt that every family needed.

But it was not to be. Less than three years after her final term ended, Jo had married Jack Maynard, one of the doctors at the sanatorium founded by her brother-in-law, Jem Russell. And the following year was to see the start of the Maynards' remarkable family.

Joey and Jack had known each other for several years, Jack having arrived at the Sonnalpe sanatorium when Jo was only fourteen. In fact it is not unlikely that the two could have met even before that, since Jack was twin brother to Mollie Maynard, one of the first mistresses at the Chalet School; and Miss Maynard had more than once invited the Bettanys and Robin

Humphries, Jo's little adopted sister, to spend a holiday at Pretty Maids, the Maynard family home in the New Forest.

Be that as it may, Jack and Joey had undoubtedly come to know each other well by the time Jo left school. Their relationship, however, had always been an easy-going comradeship between schoolgirl and grown-up. So it comes as quite a shock — both to people in the story and to some readers — when all of a sudden the two get engaged. However, before their marriage takes place, the couple share many harrowing experiences during — and preceding — their escape from the Gestapo into Switzerland; and by this point enough time has passed for everyone to grow used to the idea.

Anyway, marriage is not allowed to quench Jo's unfailingly effervescent spirits, and she continues to do things "differently". Everyone expects this, of course. So it seems well in character when her family begins with not just one baby, or even twins, but with triplets. (And, on another level, that immediately put Elinor Brent-Dyer well ahead in the school-story stakes: the grown-up heroines in other series had been quite in the habit of producing twins — one actually manages two pairs in less than a year — but no one before had ever achieved triplets.)

From the start Joey's three daughters are different in character, although they at least begin by looking very alike. In particular, all three have red hair — this to the vast amusement of Jo's elder sister, for Madge recalls that when *her* daughter Sybil arrived, some years earlier, Jo had made unflattering comments about the baby's "ginger" hair. And at first the triplets, like all new babies, have blue eyes. Later the colours begin to change, becoming, eventually, in one case grey, in another dark brown, and only in one remaining blue.

Joey and Polly Heriot (*Jo Returns to the Chalet School*)

And Joey, not content with merely having triplets, has still a few more bombshells to explode. She outrages her sister by referring to the three babies, with a perfectly straight face, as One, Two and Three – "Give me Three . . . and you can put Two back into the cradle . . .". Madge comments, that she ". . . might have known Jo wouldn't be sensible, even over her children". Later, Jo and Jack's decision to be called Mamma and Papa causes quite a stir!

The three little girls, Len, Con, and Margot, spend the first months of their lives at Les Rosiers, the villa in Guernsey where Joey and Jack had settled down soon after their arrival from Switzerland. Few details are available about this, Joey's first married home, apart from the fact that the house was in the parish of Le Forêt, although apparently not far from St Pierre du Bois. (Today, Joey might be less ready to choose this district, since the Guernsey airport is situated at Le Forêt.) In any case the Maynards have only a short time at Les Rosiers, for soon wartime conditions make it imperative for Jo and her family to leave Guernsey. First they endure a hair-raising journey across the channel; then find their way by stages to "Armishire" where, conveniently, a house has fallen vacant in "Howell Village" (see *Locations*).

This house, Plas Gwyn, is described in several books: "It was a very pretty house . . . with white walls, in accordance with its name . . . and roses and honeysuckle climbing up [them] . . . [There was a] big French window on the left of the porch . . . [and] inside the house . . . an impression of coolness and peace . . . and the scent of flowers . . ."

Plas Gwyn is to be the Maynards' home for seven or more years, and to see the birth of three boys – not triplets this time but, as

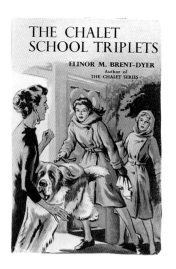

Joey often calls it, "singletons". The boys are named Stephen, Charles Richard, and Michael. (The name Charles is said to be Joey's favourite among boys' names, but interestingly it was also the name of Elinor Brent-Dyer's own father.)

By the time another move looms up, the triplets are 8½, Stephen 6, Charles 4¾ and Michael almost a year old. The boys, both in appearance and in character, are a mixed bunch. Stephen is fair-haired, sturdy, steady and dependable; Charles has black hair and very dark grey eyes; he tends to be delicate, but is in a quiet way an influential person in the family despite his tender years. Michael, almost always known as Mike, has fair curly hair and blue eyes; at times he can look like a baby angel but he is by far the naughtiest of

Joey pays a visit to the Chalet School (*Tom Tackles the Chalet School*) and is immediately surrounded by Seniors

the three.

The triplets also vary in temperament and colouring, although all three still have a strong family resemblance. Len's thick wavy hair has deepened from the original red to chestnut brown, and her eyes are now smoky grey – Elinor sometimes likens their colour to wood violets. Con has become as dark in hair and eyes as Joey herself; while Margot's short curly hair is reddish-gold and her eyes a brilliant blue. Of the three, Len is the natural leader and the most generous in nature; Con is a dreamer, and has inherited some of her mother's story-telling gifts; Margot is the family rebel, with a quick wit and a tendency to be sharp-tongued. She is also the member of the family whose health most often gives her parents cause for anxiety, for she is especially prone to bronchitis. And because Jack and Joey feel that a winter away from Britain would benefit Margot's health they agree, with the greatest reluctance on Joey's part, to let the child go to Canada for some months with Madge and Jem Russell. This separation eventually extends to a year; and in the meantime the Maynard family are compelled once again to look for another house, though in this case only a temporary one. As Miss Annersley explains to Peggy Bettany: ". . . your aunt is leaving Plas Gwyn for the present . . . No; it isn't drains like Plas Howell. It's something almost as alarming though. Part of the foundations has begun to subside, and the house isn't safe."

Luckily, a friend offers Jo the use of "Cartref", a house near Carnbach – the village on the Welsh mainland just opposite St Briavel's, and Jo is thus able to maintain regular contact with the school. The house is much smaller than the Maynards have become used to, though of course the family numbers are reduced for the time being, with Margot absent

Madge Bettany with the Robin. Joey, Grizel and Juliet look on

in Canada. And the Maynards' sojourn at Cartref does not last very long. The following spring, about six months later, the whole family is off to Canada, where Jack has "to attend an important medical conference". Here, in Toronto, Len and Con are at last reunited with their third triplet, who has grown several inches and is dramatically improved in health.

Joey, her husband, and the six children are to remain in Toronto throughout the next year; and during their stay the Maynard family is increased to eight by the arrival of twins – Felix Nicholas and Felicity Josephine – who are both silvery fair in colouring. In the meantime Len and Con have joined Margot at La Sagesse Convent School, where they soon learn "to chatter French like natives"; and parents and children alike flourish in the "crisp dry cold" of the Canadian winter.

Next, it's back again to Plas Gwyn. But not for long this time: when the Maynards arrive in Britain they find the Chalet School already in the midst of preparing to follow the sanatorium to Switzerland. And since Jack Maynard has now been appointed head of the san, this means that Joey and her flock must face a mass removal almost at once.

For Jo, the pangs of parting from Plas Gwyn, her beloved house in the Golden Valley, are tempered by the joyful prospect of returning to live in the Alps. And her new home on the Görnetz Platz (see *Locations* p. 62) certainly has much to offer:

> Jo stopped short in the middle of the broad pathway and stood gazing. She saw a very big, four-storied house with plastered walls, frescoed and banded with three balconies reaching from the ground floor to the third floor. The wooden posts

Elsie Carr and Maria Marani carrying out a bet – whether they can fit their heads through the back of a pair of chairs! Joey is seated in the foreground; Cornelia Flower, Ilonka Barkocz and Suzanne Mercier watch in amazement

were carved and the close-set railings were high enough to prevent any accidents with heedless youngsters. The deep-pitched roof was weighted with heavy stones, roped on in the usual fashion of the Alps, and there were four dormer windows set in it. Beneath came six small ones of the lattice type. The main bedroom floor had French windows opening on to the balcony, and on the ground floor there were three windows on each side of the door. The house stood on a little eminence and the front door was reached by half a dozen steps built sideways to the house . . .

[Inside] Jo found herself in a square hall with a door opening on either hand and a passage running across the back . . .

"*This* isn't a proper chalet," she said.

"As I keep telling you, it was a *pension*," her husband said, exaggerated patience in his tones. "It was built for that purpose – and very well built, too, I may add. This room on the right used to be the Speisesaal; and as it has a hatch through to the kitchen, I vote we keep it . . . [as the dining room]."

"I couldn't agree more. Then which [is] . . . the Saal [drawing room]?"

But Jack tells her she must decide for herself about that. And the moment Joey has entered a long spacious room at the back of the house, she does not hesitate: "Oh Jack! There's no question, of course! This is the one . . . How could you ask when it has that view of the Jungfrau? . . ."*

And so the huge elegant room (once the ballroom of the former "Pension Wellington") becomes the heart of the Maynard family's new home. And a name is chosen to signify the role this house is destined to play in the lives of many, even beyond their family circle: "Freudesheim"

Joey, followed by a weeping Hermann Eisen (whom she was sure was a Nazi spy), cries out to Jack Maynard and Cornelia Flower that Hilary Burn and the Robin have disappeared (*The Chalet School in Exile*)

* extract reproduced with permission from *Joey goes to the Oberland* (Chambers, 1954)

– "Happy Home".

One old friend who receives a specially warm welcome at Freudesheim is Grizel Cochrane – that same Grizel who was among the Chalet School's very first pupils. Grizel has been living in New Zealand for many years, and she has never met the latest additions to the Maynard household.

As she sits enjoying an "English tea" with Joey, a ". . . clatter of small feet . . . and the thud of paddy-paws" herald an eruption into the drawing room. Bounding ahead comes a huge golden and white St Bernard. Just for one instant Grizel's thoughts go to Rufus – the beloved St Bernard, who as a puppy was rescued from drowning by the youthful Joey, to become thereafter her faithful companion all through her schooldays and onwards.

Madge Bettany

"Joey! This isn't – but of course it isn't! I remember dear old Rufus dying when you were at Cartref. Is this a son of his?"

"No; Bruno was a gift from the school the second term we were up here. I'd been talking of having another dog, but I couldn't make up my mind to doing it. Then the girls gave me Bruno and he has his own place – though never Rufus's . . ."

Joey, followed by Eigen, clutches Rufus

Next Grizel is introduced to the ninth, tenth and eleventh of Joey's family, all born since the Maynards arrived in Switzerland. First, five-year-old Cecil – short for Cecilia Marya, the real name of Jo's adopted sister Robin Humphries, who is Cecil's godmother. Then the twins, Philippa and Geoffrey, who "will be two in June". Phil and Geoff, as they are known, are both red-headed, but Cecil has dark curly hair and black eyes.

"You always said you meant to have the

longest family of all . . ." [Grizel remarks later]. "Eleven, isn't it? I hope you're satisfied."

". . . Oh, you never know . . . [I might] think of quads as a nice round off."

But even Grizel, who has never had much sense of humour, doesn't take this threat too seriously.

Joey was of course lucky in always having excellent domestic help. As a result she seems to be spared much of the nitty gritty of housework. True, she is often pictured in the throes of looking after her numerous children; she can sometimes be seen in the kitchen or immersed in a sea of mending; she has to cope with a vast number of illnesses and childish ailments – not to mention the horrendous bouts of teething trouble which seem to afflict most of her babies; but she never apparently has much truck with sweeping and dusting – although it must have needed a deal of hard work, even in the clean air of mountain Switzerland, to keep that enormous house spick and span, as it always was. But neither did Jo have to spend hours shopping in order to replenish the family's larder. No doubt all these matters were taken care of by the faithful Anna and the co-adjutor – as Anna's assistant was always known.

It helped, too, that Joey's children were all brought up, very sensibly, to be helpful around the house from an early age. And anyway it was only during holidays that everyone was at home. Before the end of the series the Maynard girls have all become pupils at the Chalet School – with the exception, that is, of the tiny Philippa: she is not only too young but is still recovering from an attack of polio she had contracted the previous year.

Len, by this time, is finishing her second year as head girl; Margot is games prefect – still a colourful personality but all round a reformed

character; Con, not only a prefect but the editor of the school's magazine, the *Chaletian*. ("By the way . . . [the speaker is Miss Annersley] . . . you're following in your mother's footsteps. She was our first editor. I know she'll be thrilled to hear that you are the twenty-fifth . . .")

Felicity, as flaxen-haired as ever, is now quite a seasoned member of the Junior School and has ambitions to take up ballet. Cecil, who like Con and Charles is very dark in colouring, has just graduated from the Kindergarten to the Chalet School proper when the triplets begin their final term.

Joey keeps an eye out for Baby Voodoo (see *Quiz*, p. 91)

As to the boys, they all – with again one exception in little Geoffrey, Philippa's twin – attend boarding schools in England; presumably following the same path as their father and uncles, for although we are told no details about Jack Maynard's education, nor about that of Jem Russell or Dick Bettany, we can hazard a guess that all three went to English public schools.

With nine of the children away at school, there were plainly gaps at Freudesheim during term-time. Of course the house was separated from the Chalet School by only a garden's length, and the Chalet girls, both relatives and otherwise, are always in and out. The staff, too, quite often run over for a chat and some of Anna's super-delicious biscuits. Not to mention the streams of visitors who arrive continually.

In any case, even without resorting to quadruplets, warm-hearted Joey has many ways of enlarging the family group. Already, a couple of years before that conversation with Grizel Cochrane, recorded above, she and Jack had become guardians to, and indeed adopted, the three Richardsons – Ruey (full name Ruhanna), Roger and Roddy. And during the year after the school's 25th birthday celebrations, two more children were to be adopted: little Claire Mabillon – a baby abandoned when her mother was killed in a train crash; and Erica Standish, a twelve-year-old orphan from Coorg in India. The latter provides some interesting links with Jo's early life and with the missing book, *Two Chalet Girls in India* (see *Questions*, page 94). For it turns out that Jo had known Erica's mother, then Dacia Parsons; and, as she explains at her dramatic first meeting with Erica, "[Dacia and I] were great pals in Coorg . . . [That was when] I was packed off [to India] together with young Robin . . . Oh, won't *she* be thrilled to hear about all this! Rob was awfully fond of your mother."

For that matter, Robin Humphries is yet another who must be included within the Maynards' extended family: from soon after the time she arrived at the Chalet School as a motherless six-year-old, Robin had been Joey's adopted sister and the two had always been especially close.

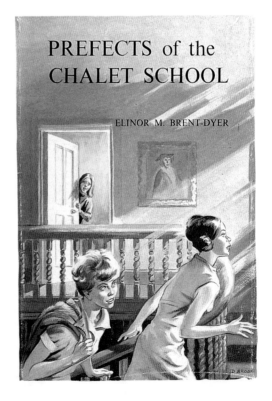

FAMILY TREE

RICHARD (Dick) Thomas Bettany
= Mary (Mollie) Patricia Avery

Margaret (Madge) Daphne Bettany
= James (Jem) Francis Russell

Josephine (Jo) Mary Bettany
= John (Jack) Charles Maynard

1) Richard (Rix) John
   Margaret (Peggy) Josephine
   = Alan ?

2) Bridget (Bride) Mary
   = Giles Winterton

3) John (Jackie) Noel

4) Maurice
   Maeve

5) Daphne

1) David James

2) Sybil Margaret

3) Josephine (Josette) Mary

4) Aline (Ailie) Elizabeth

5) Kevin John
   Kester Richard

1) Mary Helena (Len)
   Mary Constance (Con)
   Mary Margaret (Margot)

2) Stephen John

3) Charles Richard

4) Michael (Mike)

5) Felix Nicholas
   Felicity Josephine

6) Cecilia Marya (Cecil)

7) Geoffrey (Geoff) Martin
   Philippa (Phil) Anne

Nor should others be forgotten, who at various times had found a home with Jo and her family. Among them – in the earlier days, Daisy and Primula Venables, orphan daughters of Jem Russell's sister Margot Venables; the Macdonald twins, Flora and Fiona (nicknamed naughtily by Jo "Flora and Fauna"); Frieda von Ahlen, formerly Mensch, and her children; and of course Elisaveta, who was once "The Princess of the Chalet School". In later years, Adrienne Desmoines, and Melanie Lucas . . . the list could go on.

No doubt about it – Freudesheim, like Joey's previous houses with their wonderfully elastic capacity, must have been not only a happy home but a hummingly busy one.

Frieda and Bernhilda Mensch and Joey and the Robin admire the Mensches' Christmas tree

QUIZ

How many of these can you get right without reference to the books? Give yourself one mark for each question or, when a question consists of more than one part, one for each part. The total comes to thirty-five. The answers can be found on p. 96.

1. In which of the books do the following people appear:
   a) Herr Alphen
   b) Gertrud Becker
   c) Alixe McNab
   d) Vera Smithers
   e) Mr Barrass
   f) Professor Fry
   g) Matron Besley
   h) Lucia Gordon
   i) Doktor Aubock

2. a) What was Tom Gay's real name?
   b) Whom was she named after?
   c) Of whom did Tom say "She seems to think her Auntie Jo is the cat's bathmat"?

3. a) What did Joey call Margot when they first met again in Toronto after having been parted for a whole year?
   b) Why did she use the expression?

4. a) Which girl went back on a friend when the friend was fathoms deep in trouble?
   b) Who did stand by the girl?

5. How did the St Mildred's pantomimes begin?

6. a) Which girl gatecrashed the Chalet School?
   b) How did she manage it?

7. a) Which of the girls had to escape secretly when the Germans marched into Austria the year before the war?
   b) Who had to escape with them?

8. a) Who or what was Baby Voodoo?
   b) Who was responsible for his being discovered, and, with him, his creators?

9. a) Who brought her hockey stick down on Anne Montague's fingers?
   b) What did she say after she'd done it?

10. Who wrote "A volcano is a mountain that is sometimes sick"?

QUESTIONS AND ANSWERS

What happened to a book called The Chalet School Musician, *which is announced as "Coming Soon" in one of the older Armada paperbacks but never seems to have been published?*
Many people have been puzzled by this, but unfortunately there is no definite answer to the question. The one thing certain is that no story with the title *The Chalet School Musician*, either published or unpublished, has ever existed. A possible explanation might be that before publication of the second part of *A Genius at the Chalet School* (which was divided for the paperback edition) the title *Chalet School Musician* could for a time have been considered, being then abandoned in favour of *Chalet School Fete* – the title actually used. But there can be no proof, either way.

Did Elinor Brent-Dyer ever visit Switzerland before writing the books that are set in the Bernese Oberland?
The only pre-war visits Elinor made to Europe were those to Austria in 1924 and to Oberammergau in 1930. After the war she would have found it difficult to take a holiday abroad, since for many years she was tied by the demands of work, and of caring not only for her mother but for other elderly ladies who lived with them. So, although the answer cannot be an absolutely definite "No", it is unlikely that Elinor ever managed a visit to Switzerland. And making a setting for the Chalet School would have given her no problems: plenty of information was available to her in travel brochures and guide books. Her imagination supplied the rest.

Why is it that Joey, who is a Roman Catholic, can be godmother to her sister's daughter, Josette Russell, whereas Madge isn't allowed to be godmother to any of Joey's family?
It is correct that Joey is Josette's godmother; and that she tells Madge at the time of the triplets' christening, "Sorry I can't have you [as godmother], my dear, but as they'll be brought up Catholics, it can't be done". But – for once – this is not as inconsistent as it may appear. Josette is at least a year older than the Maynard triplets, and at the time of her birth it is possible that Joey was still, like her elder sister, a member of the Church of England, which would explain the apparent discrepancy. It is never made clear at what point Jo did become a Roman Catholic; nor, for that matter, why her husband should have been a Catholic at all, since his twin sister, Molly Maynard, is definitely C. of E. in all the early stories.

Why are there so many inconsistencies in the Chalet School series?
Even the most devoted fan could not deny that the Chalet books contain a luxuriant crop of inconsistencies. People change their names, their ages, their religious affiliations, and their occupations at a bewildering rate – and sometimes more than once. Place names can also change; and, even more disconcertingly, the places can sometimes remove themselves from, for example,

one side of a mountain or valley to the other (as happens to the Bärenbad mountain in the ninth story). The head girl in one book is apparently demoted to being only library prefect in the next, while the roll of past head girls varies capriciously. And so on – and on . . . All readers will have their own pet list.

Perhaps the oddest change of name is the transformation of Elise La Pâttre into Thérèse Lepâttre, which – along with the tangle of Matrons, Lloyd/Gould/Rider – has already been discussed above. Another who suffers name changes is Molly Maynard: her married name appears in three different versions. Then Mary Burnett, the Chalet School's fifth head girl (Yes, that's *right*!) is described, when she's first mentioned, as being in a form *below* Joey at the High School they both attended in England; yet, when she arrives at the Chalet School only a term later, she has apparently aged three years, thus accounting for her becoming head girl while Jo is still barely sixteen. For that matter, the town of Taverton, where that High School was located and where the Bettanys are living in the early chapters of *The School at the Chalet*, is at one point in Cornwall, yet before long finds itself across the border in Devon.

Among my own favourite inconsistencies is one that was pointed out by Miss Polly Goerres in her dissertation on "The Language, Traditions and Genre of the Chalet School Series". It concerns Clem Barras's temperamental artist father, who ends an outburst with the ringing declaration: "And mark my words it will, or my name's not Adrian Charles Barras!" And, lo and behold, four books later his name is NOT Adrian Charles Barras: he is now apparently Miles Barras, although at least he's still an artist.

Now, it is easy enough to point out the inconsistencies – it would be difficult to miss them in some cases; but, to try and explain why they arose in such profusion – that's quite another matter. The simple answer would be that Elinor Brent-Dyer had a poor memory and was an exceedingly unmethodical person. And this would be undeniable. But there are, nevertheless, points to be made in her defence. The writing of a series is a highly complicated affair. Those people, for example, who compile radio or television soap operas have to keep the most careful records of all that takes place in the story, along with card indexes giving minute details of the characters – their ages, family backgrounds, appearance, occupation, etc., etc. And nowadays any writer contemplating a series, even one of moderate length, would have to approach the undertaking in this professional way. But in Elinor's day things were different, and school-story writers had a far more casual attitude. Besides, it must not be overlooked that when Elinor began the Chalet School books she was not aiming specifically to write a series, let alone one of 59 books. Maybe she did intend to provide a few sequels to *The School at the Chalet*; but in the early stages she cannot have had the smallest notion of the enormous length her series would eventually reach. That said, it must be acknowledged that Elinor might not have organised things any better even if she had realised in advance the size of her undertaking. After all, she did manage in *Jo of the Chalet School* to describe Simone Lecoutier as Mademoiselle's *niece*, whereas in the previous book the two had been only some kind of cousins. And this happens at a point when the series contains only the two books . . .

But far more interesting than the mere existence of all these flaws is the quite extraordinary degree of tolerance that readers have shown towards them. Obviously they are not considered to be very important compared with other things – irritating at times, mildly amusing at others, and good occasionally for an hour or two's speculation in trying to sort them out. The readers' attitude recalls that taken by some families to a forgetful but well-liked relative: "Oh that's just Aunt So-and-So – she always gets things muddled; but she's the greatest fun!" And when all's said and done, Elinor does manage to keep her immense cast of characters behaving all through the stories with remarkable consistency. She may confuse their ages, and many other things about them; even at times their names. Never their personalities.

Are there any books missing from the Chalet School series?
This question is usually asked in connection either with certain gaps between the stories, or with Joey's visit to India which is mentioned in a number of the later books though not apparently related in any of

the early ones. In fact Elinor did write a full-length book about the adventures of Joey and Robin Humphries, when they went to India to visit Jo's brother, Dick Bettany, and his family. The manuscript was known still to exist in the late 1950s, but unfortunately the book was never published and the manuscript has now disappeared. This story, *Two Chalet Girls in India*, would have filled a gap that lies between *The New Chalet School* and *The Chalet School in Exile*. The other missing book is one that should have come between *The Princess of the Chalet School* and *The Head Girl of the Chalet School*, where a whole term elapses. Elinor never completed a book about this particular term; but she did leave clear indications of the form the story would have taken, along with some notes about the plot; so it has been possible to reconstruct the story although it too remains unpublished. Of the other gaps that exist in the series, one – that between the second and third books – extends to a whole year. And it can be deduced, using the children's ages as a guide, that at the opening of *Three Go To The Chalet School* about three years have passed since the end of the previous story (*The Chalet School and*

Rosalie). But it seems clear that neither of these gaps was ever filled.

Was the school where Elinor Brent-Dyer herself went as a child at all like the Chalet School?
Both "No" and "Yes" to this. Elinor attended a small private day school in South Shields, which had none of the facilities and amenities enjoyed by the Chalet School during its heyday. Nor did it have a glamorous alpine setting. And the teaching there was probably on the old-fashioned side, even for the times. On the other hand, there was in both schools a similar insistence on the importance of good manners and a disciplined attitude to work. But, at a guess, Elinor and her fellow pupils had a less exciting time than the Chalet girls!

What about the school Elinor ran in Hereford – was it at all like the Chalet School?
Undoubtedly Elinor would have liked it to be. It seems, too, that she did attempt in the Margaret Roper School to foster the ideas of international co-operation and religious tolerance that had become familiar in the pages of the Chalet School

books. And clearly the basic aims and aspirations of the two schools had much in common. Another thing they shared was their school uniform, since Elinor deliberately chose one in brown and flame for the Hereford school, exactly similar in design to that worn at the Chalet School. The girls in Hereford also took part in many of the same activities as the Chalet girls, among them the annual Christmas play; and it even happened occasionally that the same play was given at both the fictional and the real-life schools. Nevertheless, although the Margaret Roper School was moderately successful for a time, it never came anywhere near the Chalet School's league. For one thing, Elinor, despite her love of children and genuine gifts as a teacher, was simply not cut out to be a headmistress. Miss Annersley would have had much to show her.

Why is the spelling in the books sometimes TYROL and sometimes TIROL?

The first of these – Tyrol with a "Y" – was for many years the standard English spelling of the word, and hence the one Elinor would probably have accepted without question at the time she began writing the Chalet School books. However, in Germany and Austria the spelling was commonly Tirol – with an "I"; and more recently this latter spelling has been adopted in English also, being now considered more authentic. Elinor uses "Tyrol" consistently in the earlier stories, changing to "Tirol" somewhere around the twentieth story.

How many books are there altogether in the Chalet School series?

Originally the series consisted of 58 full-length stories in hardback and one shorter paperback, all published between 1925 and 1970 by W. & R. Chambers Ltd; but numbers 10, 13 and 35 of the original stories were divided for publication in Armada paperbacks, and the second part of each was then retitled. As a result the total number of different titles now exceeds the original 58/59. There were also various books connected with the series, including three annuals and a book of recipes; and the two "missing" stories, mentioned above. For complete list of titles see p. 26.

How old is Jo when the triplets are born?

This is a more complicated question than it appears. In the paperback edition of *The Chalet School in Exile* Jo is stated to be nearly 21 when her three babies arrive. But the same chapter in the original hardback edition gives her age at the time as nearly 22. The latter would really be the more consistent; for if allowance is made for a year between the escape from Austria and the Chalet School's re-opening in Guernsey, then Jo would have to be nearly 22 in the November when her triplets are born, because it is clear she was already over 20 at the beginning of *The Chalet School in Exile*. That, at any rate, is the inference to be drawn from the ages of Robin Humphries and Peggy Bettany, who are 14 and 8 respectively at this point in the story – Joey having been 12, nearly 13, when the Robin was 6, and 14½ when Peggy was born. It would also allow time for the visit Jo paid to India, described in the missing book, *Two Chalet Girls in India*. However, it seems that Elinor must definitely have wanted this particular change, for references in later books usually give Jo's age as 20 when her first babies were born.

ANSWERS

Answers to Crossword on p. 47

| | | | | | | | | | | | |
|M|A|R|G|O|T| |A|G|E|N|D|A|
|A| |U| |G| |K| |W| |U| |L|
I	N	N		R	A	I	N	Y		N	E	E
S		B	E	T	T	A	N	Y				T
I	R	M	A		S	T	Y		O	M	I	T
E		O	R	E		Y		F	L	O		
	R	O	B	I	N		S	L	A	N	G	
B		R	A	N		M		O	N	E		K
E	B	E	R		G	A	S		D	Y	K	E
N			A	M	E	R	I	C	A			E
N	E	W		A	L	I	X	E		C	O	N
E		O		I		A		L		A		E
T	H	E	K	L	A		S	L	A	T	E	R

Answers to EXTRA QUESTIONS on p. 47:

Clue 18 across: Changes for the Chalet School

Clue 41 across: The Chalet School Does It Again

Clue 7 down: The Princess of the Chalet School

Clue 15 down: The Chalet School and the Lintons

Clue 36 down: Excitements for the Chalet School

ANSWERS TO QUIZ ON p.91

1. a) *The School at the Chalet*
   b) *The Chalet School in Exile*
   c) *Lavender Leigh at the Chalet School*
   d) *Rivals of the Chalet School*
   e) *Three Go to the Chalet School*
   f) *The Chalet School and Richenda*
   g) *The New House at the Chalet School*
   h) *The Wrong Chalet School*
   i) *The Chalet School Comes of Age*

2. a) Lucinda Muriel Gay
   b) Her two grandmothers
   c) Bride Bettany.

3. a) A Bouncing Bet of a girl
   b) Because Margot had grown so much in the year they had been apart.

4. a) Florence Williams (known as "Floppy Bill")
   b) Elizabeth Arnett

5. The girls were housebound by snow in the Oberland, and planned the first one as a present to the staff.

6. a) Carola Johnstone
   b) She slipped off the liner on which she was to travel to Jamaica with her cousin Maud, and took a train from Southampton to Cardiff. She changed trains there and caught one to Swansea, where she met the Chalet School girls, returning after their holidays, and went by coach with them to Carnbach.

7. a) Joey Bettany, Hilary Burn, Jeanne le Cadoulec, Maria Marani, Lorenz Maïco, Evadne Lannis, Cornelia Flower, Robin Humphries
   b) Miss Wilson, Jack Maynard, Gottfried Mensch

8. a) Baby Voodoo was a hideous doll, with a face painted on with luminous paint. It was made of an old navy-blue jumper and a white petticoat. The Middles dangled it from the roof, one night, to frighten whoever might look out of the window.
   b) Joey.

9. a) Lavender Leigh
   b) "Now who's a baby crying for a knock!"

10. Vi Lucy.